MEN WHO MASTERED THE ATOM

ROBERT SILVERBERG brings us the full history of the atom from the alpha ray to the xi particle, and the men involved. How did man first discover the atom? Why do atoms behave as they do? What are they made of? This is the story of the chain reaction of ideas. One man's suggestions triggering new theories, new knowledge, new mysteries. In this book Robert Silverberg captures the excitement of discovery and experimentation in man's continuing quest to master the atom.

MEN WHO MASTERED THE ATOM

by

Robert Silverberg

G. P. PUTNAM'S SONS

NEW YORK

For Jonas, who knows all there is to know about nuclear physics, and for Viviane, who knows all there is to know about nuclear physicists

CONTENTS

INTRODUCTION

At half past five in the morning, on July 16, 1945, at the Alamogordo Air Base in the New Mexico desert, the first atomic bomb was detonated. While awed scientists and stunned soldiers watched from many miles away, a mushroom-shaped cloud boiled upward into the stratosphere. A tremendous roar and a great pressure wave told the observers of the terrific force of the nuclear explosion. An onlooker at Alamogordo that historic morning described the scene this way in his report to the Army:

"The effects could well be called unprecedented, magnificent, beautiful, stupendous and terrifying. No man-made phenomenon of such tremendous power had ever occurred before. The lighting effects beggared description. The whole country was lighted by a searing light with the intensity many times that of the midday sun. It was golden, purple, violet, gray and blue. It lighted every peak, crevasse and ridge of the nearby mountain range with a clarity and beauty that cannot be described but must be seen to be imagined."

Three weeks later, the people of Japan were shown that dread beauty. First the city of Hiroshima, then Nagasaki, felt the might of the atomic bomb. Thousands of people died in the bombings; thousands more suffered terrible wounds. Five days after the Nagasaki bombing, World War II came to a close with the unconditional surrender of Japan.

The atomic story is not always that grim. Less than 10 years after the first bombs were exploded, the U. S. Navy submarine *Nautilus* began a 60,000-mile voyage—equal to two and a half times the distance around the earth—using as fuel a chunk of uranium no bigger than a golf ball. If the *Nautilus* had not been atom-powered, it would have needed 720,000 gallons of oil for fuel during its 2-year journey.

And in June, 1954, the Soviet Union put into operation the world's first atomic power station, generating electricity by unlocking the might of the atomic nucleus. Two years later, Great Britain opened an atomic power plant 10 times as big, and today many countries are building or already using atomic-powered electrical plants. There are several large ones in the United States, and more will be built in the years to come.

Atomic science has proved its value in many other fields. Doctors use radioactive elements in diagnosing and treating diseases. Farmers have benefited from atomic research that has helped to develop plants better able to resist disease. Radioisotopes produced by atomic reactors are used to detect leaks in oil wells and pipes, to test the ware of engine parts in industry, to gauge the thickness of sheets of paper or metal. Each year sees some new and remarkable peaceful application of atomic energy—as well as the development of some new and colossally deadly kind of bomb. The genie in the atom holds forth the promise of destruction along with its gift of miracles.

This book is not really about atomic bombs, nor about submarines powered by tiny chunks of fuel, nor about atomic power plants. Those are all *applications* of atomic energy. The story of the use of atomic energy is a fascinating one, but it is not the story we have to tell here.

What we are concerned with in the pages that follow are

ideas, not applications. How did men first discover the atom? Why do atoms behave as they do? What are atoms made of? Those are some of the questions we will answer.

One key term of atomic science is *chain reaction,* a phrase almost everyone in the world must have heard by this time. To an atomic scientist, a chain reaction is the sequence of events that follows, under certain conditions, the splitting of an atom. Parts of one atom fly off and strike other atoms, splitting them apart, and then they in turn send out atomic "bullets" that split still more atoms, and so on. We will have much to say about this kind of chain reaction in the chapters ahead.

But the discovery of the atom involves a kind of chain reaction, too—a chain reaction of ideas. One man's suggestion triggers theories in the minds of several other men, and they in turn spur still others to new insights. The "chain reaction" of atomic theory is our subject here—the wonderful explosion of ideas that eventually made men the masters of the atom.

1

THE SWERVING ATOMS

THE ANCIENT GREEKS were the first atomic scientists. They had no laboratories, performed no experiments, built no bombs. They simply looked about them at the world, pondered it, and tried to understand what it was made of.

Each Greek philosopher had his own theory. The earliest we know is that of Thales of Miletus, who taught, about 580 B.C., that the basic substance of the universe was water. Because water was so necessary to life, Thales thought that all things were simply different forms of water. Another philosopher, Anaximenes, said that the basic substance was air. When air was thinned, it became fire; when it thickened, it turned first into water, then into solid earth. Another, Heraclitus, seeing the world constantly changing, argued that a kind of fire was the basic substance of everything: "Everything flows," he taught. "Nothing stands still. A man never steps into the same river twice."

About 450 B.C., Empedocles, a Greek born on the island of Sicily, combined all the earlier ideas into his theory of the four elements. Everything in the universe, Empedocles said,

Thales of Miletus

was formed out of varying proportions of earth, fire, air, and water. Though the idea may seem strange to us, it won many followers in its day—and its day lasted almost 2,000 years. Nearly 200 years after Columbus' voyages, the learned men of Europe were still explaining natural phenomena in terms of the four elements of Empedocles, though the idea had been somewhat altered over the centuries.

There was another theory held by certain Greek philosophers—a theory that failed to win much support in its day and eventually went into the discard heap, after a brief career. It was the atomic theory.

The first philosopher who talked of the atomic idea was Leucippus, who lived in the middle of the fifth century before Christ. We know hardly anything about Leucippus, not even the place where he was born. Not a word that he wrote has survived. We know his teachings only because of things his disciples wrote down.

Leucippus' idea was that the universe was made up of an infinite number of invisible particles, and a great deal of empty space. All these tiny particles, Leucippus said, were composed of the same basic substance—though the particles came in many sizes and shapes. Earth, air, fire, and water were not themselves basic, but were made up of particles just like everything else.

The man who adopted and improved this theory lived about a generation after Leucippus. He was Democritus of Abdera, who is often credited with having invented the atomic theory. So far as we know, he based his thinking on that of the older man. But his own contribution entitles him to an important place in the history of scientific thought.

Democritus was born about 460 B.C. His native town was Abdera, far to the north of Athens, the intellectual center of ancient Greece. Oddly, Abdera had the reputation of being a town of stupid people. That seems to have been nothing but Athenian propaganda, though, because an important school of philosophy flourished in Abdera. One teacher who came to settle there was Leucippus, and young Democritus listened carefully to his theories of the universe.

When his father died, Democritus inherited great wealth, and decided to travel and study abroad. He went to Athens, where he saw the great philosopher Socrates, but he was too shy to introduce himself. "I came to Athens and no one recognized me," he said later. Democritus then went to the ancient lands of the East, to Egypt and Babylonia and Persia, studying mathematics and the sciences. He was gone from Greece for many years.

On his return, he began to write and teach. He is supposed

to have written 72 books, but none exist now. The only fragments of Democritus' writings that we have are those quoted in the books of his disciples. We know quite well what his teachings were, however.

He had looked closely at the world. He had picked up a handful of earth, had seen how it was possible to divide and divide it again until only fine grains remained. It seemed to him, as it had to Leucippus before him, that everything must be made up of infinitely tiny particles—and that, eventually, one would come to a particle that could not be divided further.

He gave these ultimate particles the name of "atoms," from the Greek word *atomos*, "that which cannot be cut." Every substance, he said, was made up of atoms. The atoms themselves were all composed of the same material, though atoms of different substances took different forms. Atoms were invisible, he said, very hard, completely indestructible. Objects might be destroyed, when the atoms composing them moved apart, but the atoms themselves could never be destroyed. When Democritus was asked how atoms made of the same substance could comprise such different things as honey and vinegar, water and stone, fire and ice, he is said to have answered by pointing to the letters of the Greek alphabet. Out of those two dozen letters, thousands of words could be formed. "The same letters," he observed, "can just as easily be used to write tragedy as comedy."

Many later writers of the classical age preserved Democritus' teachings for us. Plutarch wrote this, about A.D. 100:

"For what does Democritus say? Substances infinite in number, indivisible, and different from each other, without qualities and unchanging, are scattered about and move in the void. When they approach each other or collide or become entangled, some of these aggregations form water, some fire, some plants, and some men. But all things are really atoms or forms as he calls them, and besides these nothing exists."

And Theophrastus, about 300 B.C., gave us Democritus' explanation of different tastes:

"Democritus, in assigning a shape to each quality, made sweet to consist of fairly large, spherical atoms. To the quality sour he assigned very large, rough shapes with many angles and no curves. The sharp [in taste], as its name implies, he regarded as consisting of atoms sharp in mass, angular, crooked, thin, and unrounded. The pungent needs atoms which are thin, angular, and bent, but rounded also. Salt is angular, fairly large, twisted, although symmetrical. Bitter is rounded and smooth, unsymmetrical, and small in size."

All of this, of course, was pure theory. Democritus never saw an atom. His agile mind devised notions of what an atom of a bitter substance *ought* to look like. His theories, offered without benefit of experimentation or laboratory observation, were often wide of the mark. But in many ways Democritus had hit on the real nature of the universe. Twenty-five centuries after his day, we have learned that all things *are* made up of atoms, that all atoms have the same basic building blocks, and that matter can never be destroyed. Democritus foresaw these ideas.

One part of his theory has been disproved only in our century. That was his idea that atoms themselves could not be divided further. Eventually, he said, one reached a particle that was uncuttable, and that was the atom. But how could Democritus have foreseen the modern smashing of the atom?

After Democritus, other Greek thinkers made contributions of their own to the atomic theory. Epicurus of Samos, who lived from 341 to 270 B.C., added the idea that atoms sometimes "swerve"—that, in their paths through the universe, the atoms now and then make unexpected and spontaneous changes in direction. This idea of swerving atoms brought an element of chance into the universe. The swerving atoms might combine in unusual forms, Epicurus said, and this capriciousness of the atoms provided infinite possibilities for change and freedom in the universe.

A Roman, not a Greek, put the teachings of Democritus and Epicurus into their final literary form. Lucretius, who lived from 99 to 55 B.C., spent the last ten years of his life writing a strange and beautiful philosophical poem, *De rerum natura,* "On the Nature of Things," which tried to explain the universe in terms of the atomic theory. Here is what Lucretius says about the swerving atoms:

"When the atoms are traveling straight down through empty space by their own weight, at quite indeterminate times and places they swerve ever so little from their course, just so much that you can call it a change of direction. If it were not for this swerve, everything would fall downwards like raindrops through the abyss of space. No collision would take place and no impact of atom on atom would be created. Thus nature would never have created anything." He compared the free swerving of the atoms to the free will of man, "whereby we follow the path along which we are led by pleasure, swerving from our course at no set time or place but at the bidding of our own hearts."

Sometimes, of course, atoms collided. When this happened, he said, they would "immediately bounce apart in opposite directions, a natural consequence of their hardness and solidity and the absence of anything behind to stop them."

Some atoms did not bounce apart when they collided. They became entangled and clung firmly. These were the sturdy substances like stone and iron. Atoms of air or fire bounced apart more freely, Lucretius wrote. The different qualities of different substances stemmed from the differing shapes of their atoms. "We see that wine flows through a strainer as fast as it is poured in; but sluggish oil loiters. This, no doubt, is either because oil consists of larger atoms, or because these are more hooked and intertangled and, therefore, cannot separate as rapidly, so as to trickle through the holes one by one."

There is much that is sound and true in this atomic theory of the ancients, along with a great deal that is fantastic and unreal. The atomic idea, though, met with steady opposition almost from its birth, and eventually became subversive and forbidden to discuss.

The first powerful enemy of Democritus' work was Plato. Democritus was teaching that everything in the universe was solid and material and real, while Plato's philosophy held that mind and spirit were the only realities, the physical world just an insubstantial shadow. Plato had such hatred for Democritus that he never deigned to mention his name when attacking him.

Plato's great pupil, Aristotle, was a man of more scientific bent than his teacher. But he, too, rejected the idea of atoms smooth and atoms barbed, atoms crooked and atoms round. Aristotle gave his allegiance to a revised form of Empedocles' old four-elements theory. Fire, earth, air, and water, Aristotle said, were really four qualities—warmth, cold, wetness, and dryness. Fire was a combination of dryness and warmth, earth of dryness and cold, air of wetness and warmth, water of wetness and cold. To these qualities he added a fifth vaguely defined material he called *hyle*, which simply means "stuff." Everything was a combination of "stuff" and the four qualities. A tree consisted of a mixture of earth, water, the fire of the sun's rays, and the air. As a tree grew, it absorbed more of the four elements from its environment. When a tree was cut down and its wood dried, the water it contained escaped, and it could then be burned. When it was burned, it was split into earth (ash) and fire, which was given off.

This theory every man could easily grasp and understand. It did not depend on the existence of invisible particles which no one could or would ever see. And so it won widespread acclaim. Backed by the prestige of Aristotle, the four-elements theory became the universal explanation of the nature of things.

After the rise of Christianity, everything that Aristotle had written took on greater importance than ever. In medieval times scientific research and speculation were forbidden, and no new thought was allowed. Aristotle's teachings reigned supreme. The old atomic theory survived—ideas, like matter itself, cannot be destroyed—but it went underground, and those who taught it did so at their own risk. Now and then a medieval philosopher who taught the ideas of Democritus and Lucretius was forced to make a public denial of their worth, on pain of being burned at the stake for heresy.

Outside the Christian world Aristotle was also highly valued, but not quite so blindly. The Arabs, who were the leading scientists of the world a thousand years ago, improved on Aristotle's ideas by adding three new elements: salt, which made things dissolve; quicksilver, which made them glisten brightly; and sulfur, which enabled things to burn.

Some of this new Arab thinking filtered back to Europe during the time of the Crusades, when soldiers returning from the Holy Land brought captured manuscripts of Arab texts. Spurred by the Arab chemical theories, a new and gaudy idea swept over Europe like a raging fever.

It was *alchemy*—the "science" of changing one substance into another. The alchemists hoped to alter the proportions of the elements in a substance in such a way as to change a "base" metal, like iron, to a "noble" one such as gold. For hundreds of years, men toiled in dark chambers, mixing foul-smelling potions in the greedy hope that dull iron would turn somehow to gleaming gold. It was a vain and foolish search, doomed to failure.

Out of alchemy, though, came chemistry—the real understanding of the elements of nature. And from the work of the chemists there grew a new atomic theory, in many ways similar to that of Leucippus, Democritus, and Lucretius. This time, though, it was based not on speculation and discussion, but on dedicated experimentation.

The chain reaction that gave man control of the atom was about to begin.

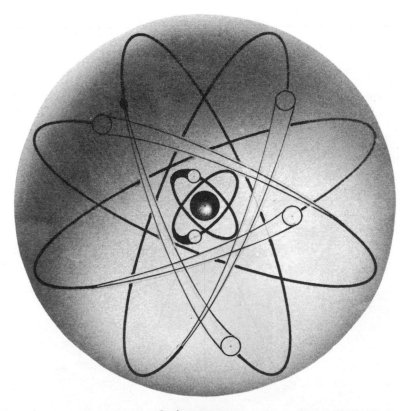

Carbon Atom

2

ELEMENTS, ATOMS, MOLECULES

THE FIRST RUMBLE of revolution against the old way of think-ing was sounded in 1661 by a witty, sarcastic, Irish-born English scientist named Robert Boyle (1627–1691). Boyle published a book called *The Sceptical Chymist*—that was how he spelled it—in which he mercilessly flayed the dreamers who hoped to turn iron into gold. Away with alchemy, he cried! Away with the nonsense of the four elements! Away with magic and tomfoolery!

Boyle helped to revive the old idea of atoms, which hardly anyone had dared speak of openly for centuries. Everything was made up of atoms clinging together, Boyle said. He placed on record his belief that all matter could be classed either as an element or a compound. An element was a substance that could not be split into a simpler substance by chemical action. A compound was a substance that *could* be split into simpler substances—in other words, a mixture of elements.

Boyle offered experimental proof to back up his thinking. He showed how two substances could be combined to form a new one that did not have the qualities of the original substances. He gave the example of iron, which is attracted to magnets. If iron filings are mixed with sulfur and heated, a compound is produced, ferrous sulfide, which is not attracted by a magnet. Boyle asked that other scientists join him in experiments that would identify the basic elements and the compounds that could be formed from them.

Science often gets detoured on false trails. The brave start of Robert Boyle did not result in an immediate understanding of the physical world because of the detour known as the phlogiston theory. This was put forth about 1700 by a German chemist, Johann Becher, and by a Prussian physician, Georg Stahl. They declared that anything that could burn contained a mysterious substance they called "phlogiston." The more phlogiston something contained, the more readily it would burn. Charcoal, for example, was almost pure phlogiston. Water had almost none.

This fantasy kept chemists busy almost a century, trying to isolate and understand phlogiston. Men spent lifetimes in the hopeless quest. Imposing theoretical edifices were constructed on this sandy foundation. For example, heat, or "caloric," was considered a substance. When something was placed over a fire, caloric entered it; when it cooled, caloric fled. Since no one could distill caloric and produce it in a flask, it was classed as an "imponderable substance," without weight or form, along with electricity and light.

Chemists went on pondering the imponderables, but in 1774 a liberal-minded English clergyman named Joseph Priestly experimented with mercuric oxide and extracted from it what he called "a surprising kind of air." He found that glowing splinters of wood would burst brightly into flame when thrust into this "air." Priestley still clung to the phlogiston idea, and gave his new gas the name of "dephlo-gisticated air."

A brilliant French chemist, Antoine Lavoisier (1743–1794), gave Priestley's gas a different name: oxygen. Lavoisier, in a remarkable series of experiments, showed that the process of combustion, or burning, consisted of the uniting of oxygen to other elements. Combustion could take place only in the presence of oxygen, and would not occur in air from which the oxygen had been removed. Combustion—which we also call oxidation—might take place rapidly, as when a gasoline tank explodes, or it might take place slowly, as when a piece of iron rusts. In both cases, though, the process is the same: oxygen combining with another element.

Lavoisier struck a deathblow at the phlogiston theory. By that notion, an object grew lighter as it burned, because it was losing its phlogiston. Lavoisier weighed a piece of sulfur carefully, then burned it. Weighing the ash that remained, together with the smoke and fumes produced in combustion, he found that the product was actually heavier! No phlogiston had been given off; rather, the burning sulfur had combined with the oxygen in the air during combustion.

The climax of Lavoisier's work came when he formulated his famous chemical law: in chemical reactions, he said, the weight of the substances taking part is the same both before and after the reaction. The products of the combustion of sulfur weighed more than the original sulfur had—but the extra weight was the precise amount of oxygen that had com-bined with sulfur during combustion. Matter might change form as a result of a chemical reaction, but no matter could be lost through such combinations. This was the first statement of what scientists have come to call the law of the conservation of matter.

Lavoisier followed Boyle in thinking that the world was

made up of combinations, or compounds, of basic elements. Through experiment Lavoisier identified 33 chemical elements. His list of elements made no mention of Empedocles' famous four. Water, he showed, was a compound of two elements, hydrogen and oxygen. Some of the other elements on Lavoisier's list were silver, gold, bismuth, carbon, copper, chlorine, cobalt, iron, mercury, lead, tin, zinc, sulfur, antimony, platinum, and nickel. None of these could be broken down into any simpler substance. By 1819, the Swedish chemist J. J. Berzelius had increased the list of chemical elements to 50.

Lavoisier might have made even greater contributions to science had he been allowed to live out his span. But he had served as a tax collector in the years just before the French Revolution, and the fury of the revolutionaries fell upon all who had served the fallen government. Lavoisier was seized in his house and brought to trial. "The Republic has no need of scientists," said the judge who sentenced him to death. The great chemist went to the guillotine twenty-four hours later. His friend, the mathematician Lagrange, remarked, "It took but a moment to cut off his head; it will take a century to produce another like it."

While Lavoisier was establishing the identity of chemical elements and explaining the nature of combustion, other men were looking into the building blocks of the universe, the atoms. Even before Boyle, the French philosopher Pierre Gassendi (1592–1655) had revived the thinking of Democritus. Gassendi suggested that the strength of iron resulted from its having rough-surfaced atoms that clung together, while water had slippery atoms. We know today that there is no truth to this notion, but at least Gassendi got men talking about atoms again.

Many researchers besides Lavoisier and Priestley helped to

push back the shroud of ignorance covering the fabric of the universe. Then came a man who drew together the thinking of many experimenters and offered an atomic theory that put the ideas of Democritus on a real scientific basis for the first time.

He was John Dalton (1766–1844), son of an English weaver. Young Dalton went to a tiny school with only one teacher, but so great was his hunger for knowledge that he studied many subjects privately, educating himself from every book he could capture. When he was twelve, the school's lone teacher retired, and the next best qualified person in the village replaced him—Master John Dalton, aged twelve! His teaching career, begun so early, was a brilliant one, and by the time he was twenty-seven he was a college professor.

Dalton's interests were extremely wide. He studied Latin, Greek, mathematics, and many aspects of science. The phenomenon of electricity interested him, as did meteorology, and he kept close records of the weather at a time when few men did so. Because he was color-blind, Dalton tried to understand that strange handicap, and as a result of his work color-blindness is sometimes still called "Daltonism" even today.

His most important work, though, was done in chemistry. Toward the end of the eighteenth century, chemists had come to see that the elements, when they combined, did so in certain fixed proportions. Ferrous sulphide, which Boyle had used as an example, always seemed to consist of seven parts by weight of iron for every four parts of sulphur. When chemists broke water down into hydrogen and oxygen, they noticed that there was always eight times as much oxygen, by weight, as hydrogen.

The French chemist Joseph Proust drew from such observations his law of definite proportions: "In a chemical combination of two or more elements, they combine in a fixed proportion by weight." This proportion never altered, Proust said. It was impossible to find water in which the oxygen outweighed the hydrogen by 10 to 1, or 20 to 1, or 5 to 1. It was always 8 to 1.*

Dalton went on to develop a second law: the law of multiple proportions. Whenever elements combined, Dalton said, the ratio of the weights of the combining elements would always be exact multiples of each other. There might be a 7-to-4 ratio, as in ferrous sulphide, or 8 to 1, as in water. But one would never find $6\frac{3}{4}$ to $3\frac{1}{2}$, or $9\frac{7}{8}$ to 1 1/16. The proportions had to be in whole numbers.

Why? Why was chemistry so neat?

Because, Dalton said, everything was made up of combinations of indivisible atoms. And if atoms were indivisible, they could combine only in whole numbers. There could be no fractional atoms. Dalton published his ideas in 1808, in a book called *A New System of Chemical Philosophy*. He stated his atomic theory in these words:

"All bodies of sensible magnitude, whether liquid or solid, are constituted of a vast number of extremely small particles or atoms of matter, bound together by a force of attraction, which is more or less powerful according to circumstances."

All atoms of a given substance, Dalton said, were identical in weight and form. To use his words: "We may conclude that *the ultimate particles of all homogeneous bodies are perfectly alike in weight, figure, et cetera.*" In other words, every particle of water is like every other particle of water; every particle of hydrogen is like every other particle of hydrogen, et cetera.

---

* Of course, Proust knew nothing of "heavy water," which has a different weight ratio, as we will see later on.

John Dalton

Dalton tried to imagine what atoms looked like. He decided that they were hard, heavy, and solid, very much like tiny billiard balls. It was as good a guess as any, for its time. Some atoms, of course, were heavier than others; in fact, Dalton thought, that was the chief difference between them. He did not think, as the ancients had, that some atoms had barbs or hooks, others were smooth and slippery.

He attempted to discover the relative weights of the various elements, which is to say the relative weights of the various kinds of atoms. To do this, he needed some sort of measuring unit. Atoms, being invisible and individually unweighable, could hardly be measured in ounces or pounds, or even fractions of ounces. Dalton had to use an arbitrary yardstick.

He chose hydrogen, the lightest of the chemical elements. One atom of hydrogen, he said, had a weight of 1. He set out to compute the relative weights of the other elements by seeing how they combined with hydrogen. By passing an electric current through water, Dalton liberated 8 grams of oxygen for each gram of hydrogen. Therefore, he decided, oxygen atoms weighed 8 times as much as hydrogen atoms.

Dalton had the right idea, but not enough information to go by, and that was why his atomic weights were wrong. He talked of atoms of compounds as well as of atoms of elements. He spoke of the "atom of water," for instance, which he thought consisted of an atom of hydrogen and an atom of oxygen.

Matters were not so simple, however. In 1811, the Italian physicist Amadeo Avogadro clarified things a little. He showed that in equal volumes of different gases there had to be an equal number of particles. When two parts (by volume, not by weight) of hydrogen were mixed with one part of oxygen, two parts of water (or, in its gaseous form, steam) were produced. Reducing this to the atomic level, it would mean that one particle of water or steam consisted of one particle of hydrogen and *half* a particle of oxygen.

But these particles could not be atoms. Dalton had shown that there were no half atoms. Avogadro demonstrated that each particle of water really consisted of two atoms of hydrogen and one atom of oxygen. In place of Dalton's confusing term, "an atom of water," Avogadro supplied the word *molecule*.

A molecule, he said, was the smallest unit of a chemical compound. Molecules were made up of atoms, the smallest units of chemical elements. A molecule might be a combination of different kinds of atoms. A molecule of table salt, for example, consisted of atoms of sodium and atoms of chlorine. But a molecule could also be a pair of atoms of the same element. Hydrogen atoms tend to form such pairs. So do oxygen atoms. When water is formed, two molecules of hydrogen and one molecule of oxygen combine to form two molecules of water. Six atoms in all are involved, two hydrogen atoms and one oxygen atom in each water molecule.

Thanks to Avogadro, it could be seen that Dalton's figure for the atomic weight of oxygen was wrong. True, the oxygen in a given amount of water was 8 times as heavy as the hydrogen. But there were twice as many hydrogen atoms as oxygen atoms in each molecule of water, so each oxygen atom was actually *16* times as heavy as a hydrogen atom!

Now that the idea of molecules was understood, it was possible to work out correct atomic weights for the elements. Once the chemical structure of a compound was known, the relative weights of its elements could be computed. Of course, the figure did not represent the real weight of an atom, but simply its weight in proportion to one hydrogen atom. Hydrogen was given an atomic weight of 1, oxygen 16. The other known elements were also given atomic weights figured on the basis of hydrogen as 1.

Many years later, it was discovered that oxygen atoms did not really weigh exactly 16 times as much as hydrogen atoms. Oxygen atoms weighed a little less, relative to hydrogen, than had been thought. It became necessary to adjust the whole scale of atomic weights. For various reasons, the atomic weight of oxygen was left untouched, at 16.00, and all other elements, including hydrogen, had their atomic weights recomputed. On this new scale, hydrogen had an atomic weight of 1.008, carbon 12.01, iron 55.85, silver 107.88, and so forth.

More precise measuring techniques, though, made even this scheme obsolete. In 1961, an international organization of physicists and chemists agreed on a brand-new scale of atomic weights. As of now, the unit is carbon, with an atomic weight of 12.000. Hydrogen's atomic weight is 1.00797. Oxygen, the one-time yardstick, now has an atomic weight of 15.9994, relative to carbon at 12. As we will see, even these elaborate calculations do not tell us the real facts about an atom's relative weight. But that part of the story must come later.

The work of Dalton and Avogadro had established the atomic theory soundly and thoroughly. Dalton had shown that everything was made up of invisible particles which combined in certain very specific proportions. Avogadro had called the particles of compounds molecules to distinguish them from the more basic units, atoms, and had proved that equal volumes of different gases contain equal numbers of molecules.

Still, no one could see an atom or a molecule. No one could separate out an individual atom and study it. The work of Dalton and Avogadro was clever, but there were many who could not accept it. To them, atoms and molecules were no more real than angels and devils—and no less real, for that matter. It was impossible to believe in what was too small to be seen. Many highly reputable scientists fought the atomic theory all their lives—physicists such as Ernst Mach (1838–1916), chemists such as Wilhelm Ostwald (1853–1932).

But the anti-atomists could offer little or nothing in the way of another explanation for the workings of chemistry and physics. The atomic theory was a logical and neat explanation. It made sense, and no one could find anything that contradicted or invalidated it. And experiments performed in the nineteenth century provided indirect proof of the existence of atoms and molecules that convinced all but the most stubborn.

By the middle of the nineteenth century, the atomic weights of the known elements had been calculated fairly reliably. But what did it all mean? Why were some atoms heavier than others? What relation was there between the atomic weights of the elements and their chemical properties?

Men studied the list of elements, trying to find some key to their relationships.

The first thing to do, obviously, was to draw up a list of the elements and hunt for patterns of resemblance. In 1865, an English chemist named John Newlands prepared such a list and discussed it at a meeting of the English Chemical Society. Newlands noticed something curious: that every eighth element seemed to have properties that were similar.

Newlands started with hydrogen, the lightest of the known elements. He counted off—hydrogen, lithium, beryllium, boron, carbon, nitrogen, oxygen. The eighth element on his list was fluorine. He grouped it under hydrogen and went on counting. Sodium, manganese, aluminum, silicon, phosphorus, sulphur. Then he came to chlorine. Chlorine very much resembled fluorine chemically. He set it down under hydrogen and chlorine.

By counting off every eighth element, Newlands found he had built up an interesting list of elements, most of which were rather closely related chemically. His first "octave" of elements included hydrogen, fluorine, chlorine, copper (grouped in one place with nickel), bromine, palladium, iodine, and platinum (grouped in the same place with iridium). Fluorine, chlorine, bromine, and iodine were all chemically similar to one another. Copper, nickel, palladium, iridium, and platinum formed another group of chemically related elements.

The odd thing was that Newlands could start almost anywhere and find these groups of eight. The second element in the list was lithium, a soft, whitish metal that reacted violently with water. Seven elements along came sodium, a very similar metal. Another seven elements and Newlands had potassium, a metal much like lithium and sodium.

Of course, some elements did not seem to fit into the scheme at all, and very often Newlands found he had to group his elements by nines or tens, rather than eights, to make the arrangement show the kinships. He had to make so many little adjustments in the system that it was sometimes hard to tell there *was* a system. But Newlands thought he had come upon something significant. "The members of the same group of elements," he said, "stand to each other in the same relation as the extremities of one or more *octaves* in music."

The learned gentlemen of the English Chemical Society laughed at him. The chemist Carey Foster asked Newlands, "Have you ever tried classifying the elements in the order of the initial letters of their names?"

Newlands dropped his research there. But other men, knowing nothing of Newlands, were working along the same lines. In Germany, the chemist Lothar Meyer was drawing up a classification of the elements; in Russia, the chemist Dmitri Ivanovich Mendeleev was doing the same thing. It happened that Mendeleev published his findings first, and so his is the name that we associate with the classification of the elements. But Meyer's work was of great importance, and in some ways was better than Mendeleev's.

Mendeleev, born in 1834, was the youngest of seventeen children. His birthplace was the remote, desolate town of Tobolsk, in Siberia. Russian political exiles had been sent to Tobolsk in great numbers after an attempted revolution in 1825, and one of these undertook to teach young Dmitri the fundamentals of science. He showed such interest that his mother took him to St. Petersburg, where he studied mathematics, physics, and chemistry. Though he was burly and robust, his health was never good, and his heavy program of studies undermined his strength. He was given six months to live unless he fled the rugged St. Petersburg climate.

In the Crimea, far to the south, Mendeleev regained his health. He received a teaching appointment, and then permission to go to France and Germany to do advanced scientific study. In such scientific centers as Paris and Heidelberg, the rough-mannered, uncouth Russian met the great chemists and physicists of his time and made himself master of all the latest scientific knowledge.

When he returned to Russia, he was recognized as the leading scientist of that not yet science-minded nation, and before he was 32 he held the rank of full professor at the University of St. Petersburg. Now he began his great work on the classification of the chemical elements.

Sixty-three elements were known, though one of them, fluorine, had so far been found only in combination with other elements. Their atomic weights ranged from 1 (hydrogen) to 238 (uranium). There were gases like oxygen, hydrogen, and nitrogen; liquids like bromine and mercury; solids like carbon and silicon. There were metals that were hard, like iridium, and some that were less hard, like gold, and some so soft they could be cut with knives, like sodium and potassium. The elements were of many colors, many textures. They had widely varying chemical properties. Was it possible to bring any order out of them?

Mendeleev wrote the name of each element on a card, along with its chemical properties and atomic weight. He took his 63 cards and pinned them on the wall of his laboratory in the order of their atomic weights. Then he looked for patterns of chemical resemblance.

He noticed the same thing that Newlands had seen a few years earlier—that every eighth element seemed to be related. The pattern was *periodic*—that is, the chemical properties repeated themselves periodically, after each seven elements.

Leaving hydrogen aside, Mendeleev arranged the next seven elements—lithium, beryllium, boron, carbon, nitrogen, and fluorine—in a horizontal row. Then he started a new row, with sodium under lithium. He put magnesium, aluminum, silicon, phosphorus, and sulfur into place. Chlorine came next, right under fluorine, which its resembled so closely.

Mendeleev was startled to see that, as he kept going, the relationships held. The third row of seven began with potassium, clearly a "cousin" to lithium and sodium. Rubidium and cesium also landed in that first column, which was as it should have been. In the seventh vertical column, bromine and iodine had fitted themselves in under fluorine and chlorine. Sometimes the elements in the columns were not closely related, though. And now and then, he had to leave a blank in order to make his arrangements come out. He wondered whether his work had any real meaning, because of these blanks. After all, if you stuck in blanks here and there as you needed them, you could create any arrangements you wanted!

There were many blanks in the scheme by the time Mendeleev had arranged all 63 of his elements. But he noticed an interesting thing about the chemical properties of each of his groups. In the first vertical group, every element united with oxygen in proportions of 2 to 1. In the second group, the elements combined with oxygen atom for atom. In Group III, the proportion was 2 to 3. Mendeleev sensed that his arrangement was far from arbitrary.

He checked now for errors, and found one almost immediately. Iodine's atomic weight was 127, and tellurium's 128. But in order to make iodine fit into the fluorine-chlorine-bromine column where it so obviously belonged, Mendeleev had placed it *after* tellurium. If tellurium really had an atomic weight of 128, his whole system had to be scrapped.

Mendeleev jumped to a bold conclusion. The system, he said, was correct. It was the figure for tellurium's atomic weight that had to be wrong! "The atomic weight of tellurium," he wrote, "must lie between 123 and 126, and cannot be 128." A bold conclusion indeed—but later work showed that he was right, and the old atomic weight of tellurium was in error.

He hit the same situation further down the list, placing gold, whose atomic weight was thought to be 196.2, **after** platinum, which supposedly weighed 196.7. Again, Mendeleev turned out to be right; gold really *was* higher in the scale of atomic weights than platinum!

He looked now at the blank spaces he had left. There were more than a dozen blanks altogether. Most of the spaces between lead and uranium were blank, six in all. And there were other gaps earlier in the list.

One of these gaps lay in the column headed by boron. Mendeleev predicted that a still-undiscovered element would fit there, chemically similar to boron. He gave it the temporary name of eka-boron, *eka* being the Sanskrit word for "one." Another gap, below aluminum, he assigned to an element dubbed eka-aluminum. A third blank, below silicon, Mendeleev said would be filled one day by an element he called eka-silicon.

In 1869, Mendeleev went before the Russian Chemical Society and read his paper, "On the Relation of the Properties to the Atomic Weights of the Elements." He had made no experiments, he said; he had simply studied the tables of the elements until a pattern emerged. There was, he said, a *periodicity* of properties apparent when the elements were arranged by atomic weights. "Certain characteristic properties of the elements can be foretold from their atomic weights," he said. "The magnitude of the atomic weight determines the character of the element." And he startled the gathering by declaring, "We must expect the discovery of many yet *unknown* elements," and then going on to predict that three of these unknowns, when found, would resemble boron, aluminum, and silicon!

Mendeleev must have seemed like some wild-eyed prophet as he boomed forth these strange assertions. No one knew whether his ideas could be taken seriously. But then, a year later, Lothar Meyer of Germany published his own table of the elements, arrived at independently, and it was almost the same as Mendeleev's. The Russian made some revisions in his table after the appearance of Meyer's. Chemists and physicists round the world began to appreciate the importance of the achievement of the periodic table. For the first time, some order and organization had been brought into the field.

Then, in 1875, a French chemist named Lecoq de Boisbaudran examined some zinc ore from the Pyrenees and found that it contained a substance unlike any ever studied before. It was a metal much like aluminum, but of a heavier atomic weight. Mendeleev's prophetic abilities were stunningly confirmed, for this was none other than the predicted eka-aluminum! Boisbaudran, using the privilege that belongs to the actual discoverer of a new chemical element, named his find *gallium*.

Soon after, a German chemist discovered Mendeleev's eka-silicon. Mendeleev had predicted an element with an atomic weight of about 72; the German, Winkler, isolated a grayish-white substance with an atomic weight of 72.3. In every other way, it matched Mendeleev's prediction. Winkler called the new element *germanium.*

Two more years and eka-boron was tracked down in Scandinavia. It fit between calcium and titanium in the horizontal row that started with potassium, just as the Russian had said. Its finder, Nilson, gave it the name of *scandium.* There could be no doubt now that Mendeleev's bold prophecies had been solidly based. An American scientist declared, "The periodic law has given to chemistry that prophetic power long regarded as the peculiar dignity of the sister science, astronomy."

The other blanks in Mendeleev's table began to fill rapidly. There was some confusion about the elements whose atomic weights ranged from 138 to about 175. A few elements in this range were known—cerium, lanthanum, terbium, erbium. Their chemical properties were so similar that in the first periodic tables they were all grouped in the same space, that of lanthanum. But in the 1870's and 1880's it was found that a great many elements indeed had been crammed into that one space. Close examination of the known elements of that type revealed a number of new ones that could be separated out of supposed elements. In quick succession such elements as holmium, thulium, ytterbium, samarium, gadolinium, and neodymium were added to the list. More were found later; there are 14 elements in the group altogether, known as the "rare earths," though some of them are not so rare at all. (There is more cerium in the earth, for instance, than there is silver or gold.) Because they are chemically so similar, the rare-earth family still occupies a special box all its own in the periodic table.

A whole new series of elements emerged next that Men-

Sir William Ramsay

deleev had not even included in his list. In August, 1868, while the Russian was still pondering his cards, English astronomers had noticed the presence of an unknown gas in the sun. During an eclipse, they passed the light coming from the fringes of the sun through a spectroscope and discovered an orange-yellow line that did not correspond to any known element. (Viewed through a spectroscope, each element when in the form of gas gives off light in lines of colors unique to that element.)

The new element was given the name of *helium*, from the Greek *helios*, "the sun." Not for many years, though, were chemists able to isolate helium on earth. Eventually, late in the nineteenth century, it was recognized that helium was the lightest of a group of new elements, invisible and odorless gases that did not combine with any other elements. Today six of these elements, the "noble gases," are known—helium, neon, argon, krypton, xenon, and radon. They occupy a group of their own in the revised periodic table.

Certainly Mendeleev must have relished the increase in the number of elements, since each new discovery only confirmed the wisdom of his great idea. He became an international celebrity, traveling from country to country to receive acclaim. Yet in 1884 when Sir William Ramsay, the man who first isolated helium, met him at a dinner, Ramsay described the great Russian scientist as "an outlandish creature," calling him "a peculiar foreigner, every hair of whose head acted in independence of every other."

Outlandish or not, Mendeleev was famous and important. He became involved in social reform, and worked to ease the despotism of the Russian Czar. Though Mendeleev often criticized the government openly, the Czar could do nothing to silence him because of his world-wide fame. In old age, a majestic, bushy-bearded figure with startling blue eyes, he was a powerful force for liberalism in a Russia that would soon be rocked by bloody revolution. When he died, in 1907, there were 86 elements listed in the periodic table, each in its proper place thanks to his remarkable insight into the patterns of the universe.

The nineteenth century had been a time of striking progress in the understanding of the physical and chemical structure of things. Dalton had revived the atomic theory and had bolstered it with experimental demonstration. Avogadro had improved and clarified Dalton's work. Many other men had helped to polish the atomic concept. Finally, Mendeleev had shown the relationship between the chemical properties of the elements and their atomic weights. No one who studied Mendeleev's table for long could go on doubting that there were such things as atoms. The weight of evidence was too great. Even if atoms were invisible, the whole scheme that now existed was too logical to deny. Everything fit together smoothly.

As the amazing century entered its final decade, almost everyone agreed that the real work of atomic chemistry had already been done. The nature of the universe was revealed. Everything was made up of hard, solid, indivisible atoms. All that remained to do was compute the atomic weights a little more accurately, tidy up some minor loose ends here and there. The basic theoretical work was complete.

Or so it was thought. But then, a double-barreled explosion of experimental discovery showed everyone that atomic science was only beginning, that the hard questions were anything but answered.

3

RAYS AND MORE RAYS

THE MAN who tore apart the neat structure of nineteenth-century atomic theory was hardly a wild-eyed revolutionary. Tall, bearded, soft-spoken and scholarly, he enjoyed the calm and quiet of his laboratory, where he sought patiently for a deeper understanding of the mysteries of science. He was Wilhelm Konrad Roentgen (1845–1923), Prussian-born, a professor of physics in the Bavarian town of Würzburg.

Roentgen carried out his historic experiments late in 1895, and presented his first public report on December 28 of that year, at a meeting of the Würzburg Physical and Medical Society. What had he done seemed quite unbelievable. He had discovered certain strange rays which had the power of passing through solid objects the way sunlight passed through a windowpane. By photographing the "shadows" cast by these new rays, Roentgen said, it was possible to see the internal structure of solid objects. By way of demonstrating, Roentgen set up a special screen on the podium. He turned on his machine. Nothing seemed to be coming from it, for the rays were invisible. But as Roentgen put his hand in the path of the rays, the image of his hand's bones appeared on the screen! The members of the society must have blinked in disbelief. But a photograph was taken, and there it was: the bones of Roentgen's hand, shown as clearly as though all the flesh had been stripped away.

Roentgen called his new rays "X rays," because their source was unknown and mysterious. And X rays they still remain, though their mystery has been revealed.

Roentgen had been doing research into electricity when he stumbled onto X rays. Men had been fascinated by electricity since the days of Thales and Democritus in ancient Greece. It had been found then that amber, when rubbed with a woolen cloth, had the strange ability to attract light objects to itself. For twenty centuries, no one had any explanation for the phenomenon. But in the sixteenth century, William Gilbert, Queen Elizabeth I's private physician, studied it and gave the occurrence the name "electricity," from *electron*, the Greek word for amber.

The kind of electricity produced by rubbing amber became known as *static electricity*. ("Static" refers to anything not in motion.) Static electricity, it was found, builds up an electric charge which is discharged all at once, when a spark of electricity jumps from the charged object to an uncharged one. There were many experiments in building up charges of static electricity through friction. It became known that a glass rod rubbed with silk would also develop an electric charge. A comb could be charged by drawing it through hair. Once charged, an object would pick up little bits of paper or other small things, and if it were done in the dark, the tiny electric spark could be seen.

There were some odd puzzles, though. If a little ball made

from the pith of a twig were dangled from a thread and you brought an electrically charged comb near it, the pith ball would swing toward the comb. But if you actually touched the comb to the pith ball, it would no longer be attracted to the comb. It would tend to swing away if the comb were again brought near it.

You could now take an electrically charged glass rod and hold it near the pith ball. Surprisingly, the ball would swing toward the rod! If you touched the rod to the ball, however, the ball would thereafter swing away from the rod.

To explain all this, scientists in the seventeenth century developed the idea of "electrical fluid." There were, they said, two kinds of electrical fluid. Combs tended to contain one kind, glass rods another kind. Each type of electrical fluid was attracted toward objects containing the other type, and repelled by objects containing its own type. When you touched the comb to the ball, some of the comb's electrical fluid went into the ball, and it would then be repelled by the comb. But the rod, containing the other sort of fluid, would attract the ball. Touching the rod to the ball changed the electric charge of the ball again, making it repel the rod.

Benjamin Franklin, who in 1752 carried out the famous kite experiment that proved that lightning was a form of electricity, simplified this theory. Instead of two electrical fluids, there was only one, he said. There were two *kinds* of electricity, though—positive and negative. If an object had too much electrical fluid, it had a positive charge; too little, a negative charge. Although we no longer talk about "electrical fluid," this is basically a correct explanation of electrical happenings.

Negatively charged objects would attract positively charged ones and would repel other objects carrying a negative charge. In electricity, opposites attracted, likes repelled. The comb, rubbed through hair, picked up a positive charge. The pith ball began neutral, without any charge. Touching the comb to the ball gave the ball a positive charge. That made it attractive to the glass rod, with its negative charge. Touching the rod to the ball now gave the ball a negative charge too, and so on.

Scientists of the early nineteenth century developed better ways of producing electrical sparks, and research proceeded rapidly. Since 1705, it had been known that when electrically charged amber was enclosed in a glass vessel from which most of the air had been withdrawn, the amber gave off a faint glow. Fifty years later, it was found that an electrical spark passing through such a partly evacuated glass tube also gave off light. During the next century, men designed better tubes to study this strange fact.

A big step forward came in 1854, when a German glass-blower and instrument maker named Heinrich Geissler constructed a new kind of vacuum pump that made it possible to remove almost all the air from a glass tube. Geissler built glass tubes and pumped the air from them. At each end of the tube, Geissler mounted an *electrode*—a metal plate. One electrode was positively charged, one negatively charged. (A negative electrode is called a *cathode*; a positive one, an *anode*.)

Geissler allowed various gases to enter his tubes. Then he sent an electric current from one electrode to the other. Lovely colors glowed in the tubes. Geissler's tubes were the ancestors of the colorful neon signs used everywhere today. But even when no gas at all was in the tube—when it was practically a vacuum within—a greenish glow could be seen on the walls of the tube near the cathode. It was thought that the glow was caused by radiation coming from the cathode—which thus became known as "cathode rays."

The man who gave them that name was an English

physicist, Sir William Crookes. He built a better vacuum tube, with a vacuum 75,000 times greater than Geissler could manage. In this highly evacuated tube, a faint green glow could still be seen on the glass where the rays coming from the cathode struck. The radiation traveled on a straight line when undisturbed. But if a magnet were placed near the tube, the glow would move about and follow the magnet. That proved that the cathode rays had an electric charge, for otherwise the magnet could not deflect them. When a metal plate bearing a positive charge was placed beneath the Crookes tube, the spot of radiation moved toward it. So the cathode rays had a negative electrical charge.

Another who experimented with these rays was the Hungarian physicist, Philipp Lenard. He built a Crookes tube that had a tiny "window" of thin aluminum. Lenard discovered that the cathode rays would pass through this window and out of the tube, for a short distance.

In October, 1895, Roentgen began to study cathode rays too. He used a Lenard tube, large and pear-shaped, with two electrodes sealed into it. To protect the tube and shield it from light that would make the glow of the cathode rays hard to see, Roentgen wrapped it in a cardboard jacket covered with tinfoil. He attached the electrodes to an electrical generator and sent a current through the tube. Placing a cardboard screen coated with barium platinocyanide, a phosphorescent paint, next to the aluminum window, Roentgen repeated Lenard's experiment. Cathode rays came through the window and caused the paint to glow.

Next, on November 8, 1895, Roentgen took a Crookes tube, one which had no window through which cathode rays could pass, and wrapped it completely in a jacket of black cardboard. He wanted to see if cathode rays could somehow escape through the glass walls of a tube, as well as through an aluminum window. He darkened his laboratory and sent electricity through the tube.

He was startled to see a ghostly greenish flickering light, about three feet from the tube! He shut off the current and the light winked out. He turned the switch on again, and the light returned. What was this? He already knew, from experiments with the Lenard tube, that cathode rays could reach only a few inches outside a tube. What could possibly be causing this greenish glow a full yard away?

Striking a match, Roentgen peered around. There, on his workbench, lay his cardboard screen from the other experiment, still coated with barium platinocyanide. Some sort of radiation must have emerged from the tube, and, striking the chemical coating of the cardboard, caused it to phosphoresce.

In the darkness, Roentgen switched his apparatus on again. He picked up a book and held it between the tube and the cardboard screen. The glow still appeared. He waved his hand back and forth between tube and cardboard. Still the glow. The rays coming from the tube could pass through solid matter as if it were not there, and striking the barium crystals on the cardboard, could make them give off light.

Since "X" was the usual mathematical symbol for an unknown quantity, Roentgen called his new rays "X rays." For the next seven weeks, he experimented systematically with the rays, playing with them the way a child might play with a shiny new toy. He discovered that when X rays were allowed to come in contact with photographic film, the film turned black when developed, just as exposure to ordinary light would make it do. Wrapping a piece of photographic film in black paper to protect it from light, he put a metal key on it, and let X rays stream over it. When he developed the film

Roentgen found that it was black everywhere but where the key had lain. The heavy metal of the key had blocked the rays from reaching the film, leaving an outlined image of the key against the surrounding blackness.

Roentgen next made an X-ray photograph of his hunting rifle. The metal parts showed up clearly on the film. (Today such X-ray examination of machinery is common, to detect internal flaws.) The scientist now persuaded his wife to hold her hand under the X rays for fifteen minutes, with photographic film beneath it. The bones of her hands stopped the rays, but the fleshy part did not, and the result was a photograph of Mme Roentgen's hand bones. Holding a hand against a screen painted with barium crystals provided the same effect without the need for photography. As Roentgen later wrote, "If the hand be held before the flourescent screen, the shadow shows the bones darkly, with only faint outlines of the surrounding tissues." Where the X rays struck the barium crystals, flashes of light were given off. Where most of the X rays were stopped by bone, no glow appeared.

After nearly two months of hectic work, often sleeping and eating in his laboratory and sometimes neither sleeping nor eating, Roentgen felt ready to make his discovery public. He read his paper, "On a New Kind of Rays," at the now-famous meeting in Würzburg on Dec. 28, 1895. Four days later, he sent some of his X-ray photographs to scientific friends, who took them to Berlin for the fiftieth anniversary meeting of the Berlin Physical Society, on Jan. 4, 1896. These incredible photos showed the skeletal structure of a human hand, the needle of a compass through its case, and a set of weights within a closed box. The next day, the newspapers published the story, and within a few weeks scientists in many countries were repeating and confirming Roentgen's experiments.

In less than a month—on February 3, 1896—X rays were

used in medical diagnosis for the first time. Two professors at Dartmouth College used X rays to take a photograph of a young man's broken arm. A twenty-minute exposure gave them a picture of the fracture and allowed them to set it properly.

The world buzzed with talk of the new rays. Where did they come from? What gave them their penetrating properties? They were something like light, but yet different. All anyone knew, in 1896, was that when an electric current was passed through a vacuum tube, radiation was given off that could make barium crystals glow brightly. Since nobody really knew what an electric current itself consisted of, nobody could form any very clear opinion about the rays it produced.

Many men puzzled over the new rays, including Roentgen himself. He found that heavy elements tended to soak up X rays while light ones let them pass. Lead, one of the heaviest of the elements, was an excellent shield for X rays. A sheet of lead less than 1/10 inch thick could absorb just about all the X rays produced by his tube. He tried to see what happened when X rays were absorbed by matter—particularly if heat was produced. His instruments were not sensitive enough, and he could not detect any heat. We know today that heat is indeed given off when X rays strike matter that absorbs them.

When the Nobel prizes were awarded for the first time, in 1901, Roentgen was given the award in physics. (Lenard, who invented the tube Roentgen used, won the Nobel prize four years later.) Roentgen lived on to see the mystery of his X rays penetrated, if not entirely revealed. Shortly before his death in 1923, he said, "I still prefer to leave the well-worn path and clamber over bramble and stone. If I should ever be missing, do not search for me on the main road."

Another who preferred to leave the well-worn path was the

French physicist Henri Becquerel (1852–1908), who was involved in the "chain reaction" of ideas touched off by Roentgen's lucky discovery. Becquerel was the son of a distinguished French physicist who had investigated the phosphorescent substances—those which, when exposed to sunlight, subsequently glowed for a while in the dark. Becquerel's own laboratory contained specimens of many phosphorescent substances. When he heard, in January, 1896, of Roentgen's work, Becquerel decided to see if there were any link between X rays and phosphorescence.

Becquerel's father had experimented with phosphorescent crystals of uranium salt. Becquerel wrapped a photographic plate in black paper and placed upon it a crystal of the uranium salt. For four hours, he exposed this to the winter sunlight. Then he developed the plate and found the outline of the uranium crystal on the negative. He tried again with a coin, then with a metallic screen pierced with an openwork design, placing the object between the plate and the uranium crystal, and each time the uranium made a "photograph" of the object on the plate.

Becquerel concluded that the sunlight caused the uranium to give off X rays, which darkened the photographic plate around the object placed on it. On February 26, 1896, Becquerel prepared a photographic plate as usual for an experiment, but the day was sunless. He put the plate in a drawer, with its uranium crystal still resting on it. Over the next few days, no more than a faint glimmer of sun cut through the clouds. On March 1, Becquerel decided to develop his plate anyway, thinking it might have at least a weak trace of a silhouette.

"The silhouettes appeared, on the contrary, with great intensity," Becquerel wrote later. Amazed to find that the uranium crystals seemed to be giving off radiation in the absence of sunlight, Becquerel tried a new experiment. He put a uranium crystal on a photographic plate, choosing a crystal that was curved in such a way that it touched the plate only in a few places. Alongside it on the same plate he put another bit of uranium salt, separated from the sensitive plate by a pane of glass. He did all of this in a darkened room so no light at all could strike the plate or the uranium crystals. Finally, he put the plate inside a cardboard box, put that within a second box, and hid the whole experiment away in a drawer. He also put a second plate, wrapped in aluminum, in the drawer. After five hours, he took the plates out and developed them.

They both showed the imprint of the crystals! Even in the darkness, the uranium had given off rays which, penetrating glass or aluminum as though nothing were there, could make an outline on a photographic plate!

This was not phosphorescence, since sunlight was necessary in order to make substances phosphoresce. Nor was it Roentgen's X rays, which were produced by electric currents. This was something new and different—a *spontaneous* ray, given off by the element uranium! Uranium, the heaviest of the known elements, had been discovered in 1789, but no one before Becquerel had thought of looking for such an effect.

On March 2, 1896, Becquerel announced his findings to the French Academy of Sciences. For the second time in eight weeks, the scientific world was jolted by the news of an inexplicable new radiation—first X rays, now the rays Becquerel called "uranic rays." Mystery upon mystery!

Becquerel's discovery made the whole structure of atomic theory, almost a century old, totter. Dalton and all who followed him had held that atoms were unchangeable and eternal. But, according to the laws of physics, anything that gave off energy had to undergo change. If atoms of uranium were really radiating energy constantly—as Becquerel's experiment seemed to show—then uranium atoms were unstable, spending their substance. Energy could not come from nowhere.

Was it possible? Could the eternal atom actually give off energy, and decay?

Roentgen's work with X rays had led Becquerel, almost immediately, to discover another sort of radiation. And Becquerel's work threatened to upset everything men thought they knew about atoms. The chain reaction was under way. It was necessary now to verify Becquerel's work and to see if there were other elements that also gave off "uranic rays."

The scientist who accepted this challenge holds a unique and romantic position in the story of the atom. At a time when most women were content to learn to read and write and tend to household chores, Marie Curie, the heroine of science's greatest love story, achieved breathtaking insight into the nature of the atom, and won an immortal place in the history of science.

She was born in Warsaw, Poland, in 1867. Blonde, pretty Marie Sklodowska was the daughter of a physics teacher, and she was no more than four when she began to wander into her father's little workroom to be shown the gleaming, fascinating scientific instruments.

In the Poland of a century ago, girls were not considered in need of higher education. Universities were closed to them. Marie, her curiosity whetted by her father's textbooks, longed to study physics and mathematics, but no opportunity was available in her homeland. In her teens, she took a job as a governess for young children, and saved every penny she could spare so that she could afford to go to France, to study at a university. Her father helped her with whatever he could put aside from his small salary.

Marie was twenty-four, in 1891, when she finally had enough money to go to Paris. She planned to be gone only two or three years, and then to return and teach in her native land. Traveling cheaply on third- and fourth-class trains, she made the three-day journey and registered in Paris' great university, the Sorbonne. For a few months she lived with her married sister Bronya, who had earlier gone to Paris to study medicine. Then, because she felt she had to live alone to concentrate properly on her work, Marie moved to a cold, dismal attic room near the Sorbonne. For three years she lived a life of hunger and privation, hardly noticing her discomforts as she pursued her studies. A crust of bread, a cup of tea, saw her through long evenings of work in her lonely room, six flights of stairs from the street. She was graduated with the highest honors in 1894, and received a scholarship to do advanced research.

Her idea of returning to Poland vanished soon afterward. While visiting a Polish professor living in Paris, Marie met thirty-five-year-old Pierre Curie, a shy, brilliant man who had had a master's degree in physics at eighteen, and who now was chief of the laboratory at the School of Physics and Chemistry of the City of Paris. Pierre Curie was willing to make his laboratory available to Marie for any experiments she wanted to conduct. But more than a scientific interest linked the two.

Marie later wrote of this first meeting, describing Pierre as "a tall young man with auburn hair and large, limpid eyes. . . . I noticed the grave and gentle expression of his face, as well as a certain abandon in his attitude, suggesting the dreamer absorbed in his reflections."

They saw a great deal of one another in the fall of 1894.

Pierre had once written in his diary, "Women of genius are rare," but he recognized that rare quality in Marie. "We were both convinced," Marie wrote many years later, "that neither of us could find a better life companion." In July, 1895, Mademoiselle Marie Sklodowska became Madame Marie Curie.

They lived in a small apartment near Pierre's laboratory. Marie learned to cook and keep house—while doing research on her current topic, the magnetic properties of steel. That subject occupied her for several years. She completed her work on it in the fall of 1897—soon after the birth of her first daughter, Irène, on September 12, 1897.

Early in 1896, the discoveries of Roentgen and Becquerel had dumfounded the scientific world. The Curies, of course, were deeply interested. They were eager to join the quest for an explanation of Becquerel's rays. But one research project must be completed before another can be begun. Not until late 1897 did the Curies start to study the "uranic rays."

Pierre arranged for Marie to have the use of a little glassed-in studio on the ground floor of the school. It was really just a storeroom, cluttered with lumber and discarded equipment, so poorly heated that on some winter days the temperature in the room dropped as low as 44°F. Madame Curie's first approach was to measure the ionizing power of uranium's rays —that is, their ability to make air a conductor of electricity. When X rays or "uranic rays" passed through air, they left it in an electrically charged state. No one knew why.

Using equipment of their own devising, the Curies measured uranium's radiation and ionizing powers. They found that the greater the amount of uranium, the stronger the powers of ionization. Neither temperature nor pressure nor the presence or absence of light governed the intensity of the radiation—just the quantity of uranium. Furthermore, it didn't matter what other elements the uranium happened to be combined with chemically. *All* uranium compounds gave off rays—so the radiation was a property of uranium itself.

Madame Curie gave a name to this radiating property of uranium. She called it *radioactivity*. And she and Pierre set out to find other radioactive elements.

It was not long before she had discovered a second one: thorium, the second heaviest of the known elements. Testing compound after compound, she found that only those containing uranium or thorium were radioactive. Now she began to go through every chemical compound she could find in the collection at the School of Physics. As her daughter Eve later wrote, "Pierre . . . chose with her the veined fragments, hard or crumbly, oddly shaped, which she wanted to examine."

One day they were examining a mineral called pitchblende, the chief ore of uranium. Testing it, they found that it was radioactive—no surprise—but they also found, and this *was* a surprise, that it was vastly more radioactive than it ought to be. Its radioactivity was nearly four times as intense as they expected.

"It must be an error in experiment," Marie said. She checked and rechecked. There was only a small quantity of uranium in the pitchblende sample, yet the radioactivity was incredibly strong. It had to be caused by some radioactive element other than uranium or thorium, then. But she had already investigated every known element.

Only one conclusion remained. Pitchblende must contain some new, unknown, powerfully radioactive element!

The Curies concentrated on finding it, though other physicists told them they must be mistaken, when they announced their belief on April 12, 1898. Pierre gave up his own research, and joined Marie in the cold, glass-walled laboratory. Their immediate goal was to find the mysterious radioactive element in the pitchblende.

Pitchblende had been mined in Austria for four hundred years. At first, silver came from the mines at Joachimsthal; later, the sought-for mineral was uranium, which was used as a coloring agent in glass and porcelain. Pitchblende was fairly expensive. But after the uranium was extracted from it, the left-over mineral was just so much waste. The economy-minded Curies got a sample of pitchblende from which the uranium had been separated. It was just as radioactive as the original pitchblende. So they wrote to the director of the Joachimsthal mines, asking if they might have some of the worthless waste. Back came word that they could have a ton of waste, free of charge, if they would pay the cost of shipping it from Austria to Paris.

The Curies got their ton of pitchblende waste. Where to store such a mountain of ore, though? Certainly not in their tiny laboratory. They found a dismal wooden shed, whose leaky glass roof admitted the rain. In the winter, cold seeped through as though the shed had no walls; in the summer, the glass roof turned the place into a veritable hothouse. Here the ton of gray-brown pitchblende waste was dumped, and here the Curies began their work.

Using acids and other chemicals, they dissolved away the nonradioactive components of the pitchblende. Day after day, month after month, they boiled and poured and stirred, ignoring fatigue and discomfort as they refined their mountain of ore. "The shed," Madame Curie later wrote, "got covered with pools of all kinds of deposits and liquids. It was exhausting work moving the heavy buckets, decanting the liquids, and stirring the boiling material in an iron pan for hours on end."

They were looking for a radioactive element similar to bismuth, but heavier. If they found it, they planned to call it *polonium*, after Madame Curie's homeland. Soon they succeeded in isolating a few specks of polonium. Yes, it was much like bismuth, and, yes, it was radioactive—far more so than thorium or uranium. But polonium was not radioactive enough to account for the unusual intensity of the pitchblende's radiation. There had to be *another* new element lurking in that mountain of waste.

More tons of pitchblende arrived from Austria. The boiling and stirring and refining continued. The Curies had given the name *radium* to the second new element they hoped to find. What they did not know was that the pitchblende contained less than one part in a million of radium, despite its fierce radioactivity.

The search lasted until 1902. Quite early in the quest, they managed to isolate a substance a thousand times as radioactive as uranium. Even this was not pure radium, though; it was mixed with another element which they identified as barium. They worked on. In 1900, they discovered that they were working with dangerous substances. Pierre Curie, experimenting on himself, took a small sample of their impure radium and held it against his arm. The skin turned red as if burned, and did not heal for almost a month. Madame Curie also received radioactivity burns, as did Henri Becquerel, who was keenly interested in the work of the Curies. Becquerel, carrying a glass tube of radioactive substances in his pocket, was badly burned. "I love this radium, but I've got a grudge against it," he told the Curies.

Though they were risking their lives, the Curies continued, in hot weather and cold, fighting an endless struggle against the natural elements as well as the chemical ones. Nearly four years had gone by before the day, in 1902, when the Curies could announce that they had isolated a visible quantity of pure radium.

Thousands of tons of pitchblende had yielded less than one one-hundredth of an ounce of radium. The new element went into one of the blank spaces on the periodic table as element 88. Uranium was element 92, thorium element 90. The element actinium discovered in 1899, was number 89. The 91st space on the table remained blank until 1917, when proto-actinium was isolated. All these heavy elements were radio-active.

The properties of radium were strange and wonderful. Not only did it give off the invisible "uranic rays" of Becquerel, but it radiatd heat, electrified the air that surrounded it, and killed any bacteria near it. In the dark, it glowed with an eerie blue-white light, turning the ramshackle shed of the Curies into a fairy palace whose crumbling walls shone with a sparkling brilliance.

Honors rained on the Curies from many nations as their work became known. The scientists had not believed anything would come of their toil, but now, as Madame Curie's daughter Eve wrote, they "could only bow before the facts, before the superhuman obstinacy of a woman." The Curies shared the 1903 Nobel Physics Prize with Henri Becquerel. But Marie and Pierre, exhausted by their years of life-draining labor, were too ill to go to Stockholm to receive their prizes, and the awards had to be sent to them in Paris.

At the moment of her great scientific triumph, Madame Curie suffered a tragic blow. In April, 1906, Pierre was run down by a wagon as he crossed a street, and died instantly. Marie was left with two small daughters, Irène and Eve. At thirty-eight, her love story was over.

But not her romance with science. Many years of life remained to her, and she worked on with furious energy, studying radium and the radioactive phenomena, teaching hundreds of pupils, setting up X-ray laboratories on the battle-front in World War I. In 1911, she again received a Nobel prize. Her first award, in physics, had honored her work with radioactivity. Now she was given the chemistry prize for her discovery of the new elements polonium and radium. She is the only person ever to win two Nobel prizes in science. Many years later, her daughter Irène would join the Nobel honor roll, for she became a great scientist in her own right. We will consider her work in a later chapter.

To the end of her life, the black-garbed Madame Curie continued her work, though plagued by illness and advancing blindness. The radioactive elements with which she worked gave off dangerous rays, as she knew, but she bore the risks for the sake of knowledge. The steady dose of radioactivity she absorbed during her career eventually killed her. When she died, in 1934, it was of leukemia, or cancer of the bone marrow. The radium she had worked so hard to discover destroyed the cells of her blood and ultimately took her life.

At the turn of the century, three astounding discoveries had demolished the smug idea that science understood the atom. Roentgen, Becquerel, and the Curies had helped to show that the atom was far from indivisible, eternal, and stable. The atoms of certain elements gave off particles. They radiated energy. They changed. The knowledge that atoms could dis-integrate spontaneously was a mortal blow to the old concepts. The atomic theory itself still stood intact. But almost every aspect of it had to be re-examined and re-interpreted. Before long, men would be looking deep within the heart of the atom.

4

PARTICLES WITHIN PARTICLES

As THE NEW CENTURY began, scientists tried desperately to fit X rays and "uranic rays" into the scheme of things. One way of beginning was to try to relate the new rays to a radiation men had long known: light.

In the seventeenth century Isaac Newton had carried out an important study into the properties of light. Newton proposed the idea that light rays consisted of a great many tiny separate particles, or "corpuscles." About the same time, the Dutch astronomer and mathematician Christian Huygens was suggesting that light moved in waves, rather than individual corpuscles.

Newton also showed, using a glass prism, that so-called "white" sunlight was really made up of a mixture of light of many colors. The prism split light up into its component colors, and made them visible as a band, or "spectrum," that showed a color transition from red, orange, and yellow through green and blue to violet. In the following century, about 1750, the device known as the spectroscope was developed—an arrangement of lenses and prisms that made possible the examination of light on a careful and exact basis.

In 1859, two professors at the University of Heidelberg in Germany, Robert Bunsen and Gustaf Kirchoff, carried out a series of experiments with a spectroscope. They burned many elements and studied the flames produced. It developed that each chemical element gave off a particular and individual pattern of lines in the spectrum—almost a "fingerprint" of the element. Each element's spectral lines were always found at the same place in the spectrum, and no other. It was in this way that the element helium was discovered in the spectrum of the sun before it was found on earth.

Why was it that each element gave off its own characteristic combination of colored light? No one knew—not yet.

Research into the mysteries of light went on. About 1814, the French physicist Augustin Jean Fresnel had performed experiments which seemed to prove Huygens' theory that light moved in waves. Fresnel was able to calculate the wavelength of light. Picturing light as a stream of undulating waves, Fresnel measured the wavelength as the distance from crest to crest or from trough to trough of each undulation. But the nature of these waves remained a mystery.

Two other major mysteries were electricity and magnetism. In 1873, the British mathematician James Clerk Maxwell sweepingly linked all three puzzles in his brilliant *Treatise on Electricity and Magnetism*, which advanced the "electromagnetic" theory of light.

Maxwell based his work on earlier research that had shown that a change in electric current gives rise to a magnetic field, and that a changing magnetic field could produce an electric current. Michael Faraday had worked out that concept, and every electric generator, motor, and transformer in the world depends on Faraday's idea. Maxwell went on to say that the changes in an electric field set up electric waves, spreading outward the way ripples do on a quiet pond when a stone is thrown into it. Since Faraday had shown that electricity and magnetism were related, Maxwell added that such an electric wave would be accompanied by a magnetic wave at right angles to it. He called the combination an electromagnetic wave. The speed of such a wave through a vacuum, Maxwell found, would be about 186,000 miles a second.

This was also known to be the speed of a wave of light. So Maxwell concluded that light was a form of electromagnetic radiation. The wavelengths of light ranged from four ten-thousandths (4/10,000) of a millimeter for violet light to seven ten-thousandths of a millimeter for red light. Maxwell insisted that other electromagnetic radiations, with different wavelengths, would also be discovered.

We can best understand what we mean when we say "different wavelengths" by looking at a few waves. Consider a gentle, slow-moving wave. The crests are far apart, and so the wavelength—the distance from crest to crest or from trough to trough—is quite long:

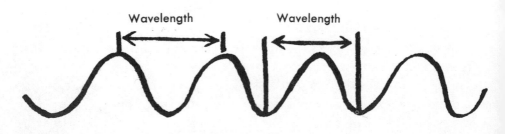

Wavelength   Wavelength

But look at this choppy, fast-moving wave. It is nervous and active, and its wavelengths are short:

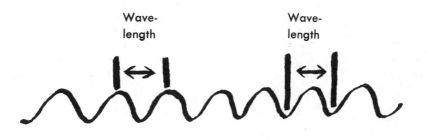

In 1887, Heinrich Hertz produced electromagnetic radiations with wavelengths much longer than those of visible light. These "Hertzian waves" had wavelengths of several inches and more. A few years after Hertz found a way to generate them, a clever Italian physicist named Guglielmo Marconi found a practical use for them, which is why we usually call Hertzian waves "radio waves" today.

The next step, now that Maxwell had wrapped light, electricity, and magnetism into one theory of electromagnetism, was to get down to fundamentals. What caused light? What was electricity?

About 1831, Michael Faraday had concluded that electricity consisted of separate units each carrying an electrical charge. Just as all matter was composed of atoms, so too, Faraday said, was an electric current made up of "atoms of electricity." But it was confusing to talk of two different sorts of atoms, so in 1891 the Irish physicist G. Johnstone Stoney coined the name *electron* for the basic particle of electricity.

Stoney and a number of others thought that the various electromagnetic waves were caused by movements of electrons in the atoms of matter. This was a startling idea, because in 1891 most physicists still clung to Dalton's picture of the atom as a sort of solid billiard ball. How could a solid and indivisible thing like an atom contain small, busy little particles such as electrons?

In 1895, the great Dutch physicist H. A. Lorentz arrived at a mathematical theory explaining the relationship between electrons and light. The Lorentz electron theory showed elaborately that light and the other electromagnetic radiations were created by vibrating electrons within the atoms of matter. The wavelength of the radiation, Lorentz said, depended on the speed of vibration.

A year later, another Dutch physicist, P. Zeeman, translated Lorentz' theory into experimental observation. He burned sodium and observed the flame through a spectroscope. He saw the familiar two yellow lines that sodium always produced. Then he switched on a powerful electromagnet. At once, each of the sodium lines split into three lines! Lorentz' theory had been verified.

The new electron theory needed one more confirmation, though: experimental discovery of the electron itself. This was provided in 1897 by the English physicist Joseph John Thomson (1856–1940).

Thomson—or "J. J.," as nearly everyone called him—was a key link in a chain of English scientists who did much to unveil the mysteries of the atom. The son of a dealer in rare books, J. J. was a shy, studious boy who originally studied engineering, taking his college degree at the age of 19. When he graduated, he received a scholarship enabling him to go to Trinity College, Cambridge, where his great scientific work was performed.

The slender, pale Thomson quickly put aside practical

engineering to study the fundamental problems of physics. In 1880, he began to investigate cathode rays and that strange greenish glow they produced in a Crookes tube, the same subject which 15 years later would lead Roentgen to the discovery of X rays. While in the midst of this research, Zeeman argued that if light was really caused by the motion of electrons in atoms, it should be possible to demonstrate it visibly. He would *change* the motion of the electrons in atoms with a magnetic field and see what happened. Thomson was given the important post of Cavendish Professor of Physics at Trinity College. He was only twenty-eight. His new professorship brought him into contact with the most promising young physicists at Cambridge, and Thomson's role as a teacher was perhaps even more important than his own accomplishments as a scientist.

Over more than a decade, Thomson studied the Crookes tube and the mysterious radiation it produced when an electric current was passed through it. The electricity, traveling through the near vacuum within the tube, somehow created a green glow in the walls of the tube. Crookes and others had decided that invisible rays emanated from the negative electrode, or cathode, and gave off the glow when they struck the glass walls of the tube.

Thomson wanted to know why.

He designed a Crookes tube that contained two electrically charged metal plates in addition to the regular electrodes. When the current was turned on, invisible radiation came from the cathode and headed for the positive electrode, or anode. A hole in the anode permitted the beam of radiation to continue through and pass between the two charged plates. Finally, the beam hit the glass wall at the end of the tube, producing the familiar green glow.

It was already known that the beam of radiation would move toward a positively charged plate. Thus the cathode rays carried a negative electrical charge. Thomson marked the end of his tube with a scale so he could measure the actual amount of deflection of the beam caused by the presence of the positive plate. The negative plate, of course, repelled the beam. By moving his charged plates around, Thomson could make the beam of cathode rays—and so the spot of light— move. He could also bend the beam with a magnet.

Thomson discovered what the cathode beam was composed of by putting a small screen coated with zinc sulfide in the path of the cathode rays. When the current was turned on, tiny bursts of light could be seen instead of the green glow. It could only mean that small particles were raining against the atoms of the screen's coating. Each burst of light was of the same intensity, suggesting that every particle hitting the zinc sulfide was identical to every other particle in the cathode-ray beam.

Through these experiments, Thomson was able to conclude that the beam from the cathode consisted of tiny negatively charged particles. At first he called them "corpuscles of electricity," but soon he adopted Stoney's word, "electrons." The speed of the electrons as they flew through the tube, Thomson found, was enormous—about a tenth the speed of light. Knowing their speed, Thomson could calculate their mass. He found that the mass of a single electron was less than a thousandth of that of the lightest atom, hydrogen! (The mass of an object is not quite the same thing as its weight. Weight can change under varying conditions; a person's weight is quite different on land, in water, or on the surface of the moon. The mass of an object is equal to its weight in a vacuum at sea level on the earth's equator. Something that has a mass of 1 ounce under those conditions has a mass of 1 ounce anywhere in the universe, whatever its weight may happen to be.)

Thomson told his colleagues about his experiments at Cambridge on April 29, 1897. He made these three main points:

" (1) That atoms are not indivisible, for negatively electrified particles [electrons] can be torn from them by the action of electrical forces, impact of rapidly moving atoms, ultraviolet light or heat.

" (2) That these particles are all of the same mass, and carry the same charge of negative electricity from whatever kind of atom they may be derived, and are a constituent of all atoms.

" (3) That the mass of these particles is less than one thousandth part of the mass of an atom of hydrogen."

These conclusions were so incredible that most of Thomson's listeners thought he was joking. Remember, Madame Curie had not yet begun her work on radioactivity. The rays of Roentgen and Becquerel were not understood at all. Thomson's suggestion that the atom could be divided, and that it somehow contained very much tinier particles than itself, seemed unbelievable.

Yet the electron theory answered many troublesome questions. Electricity could now be understood as a flow of electrons. An atom itself had no electrical charge—and so, if it contained electrons, it must also contain something else with a positive charge to balance things. But it was possible to separate electrons from an atom.

Recall the experiments with glass rods and silk cloths. Rubbing a glass rod with a silk cloth gave it a positive electrical charge. That could be explained by saying that the silk cloth rubbed electrons away from the rod. That would give the silk cloth a negative charge, and it would leave the glass rod, minus some of the electrons, charged positively. A comb running through hair would steal electrons from the hair, and thus get a negative charge. If an object had a surplus of electrons, it was negatively charged; if it had lost some electrons, it was positively charged.

Some substances tended to lose electrons easily, like metals. Other substances, like silk or wax, hung on more tightly to the electrons of their atoms.

As for an electric current, it was simply a stream of electrons. The substances that allowed electrons to pass easily through them, like copper, were good conductors of electricity. Substances that stopped electrons from passing, such as rubber or glass, were bad conductors. That was why a copper wire, when covered with rubber insulation, could be handled safely even when a strong electric current was running through it.

Thomson, by showing that cathode rays consisted of electrons, had given science a new understanding of electricity. For this accomplishment, he received the 1906 Nobel Prize in Physics. But at the same time he had helped to overthrow the old picture of the atom. He saw the atom as something not at all solid and unbreakable, but rather as a kind of positive sphere containing electrons. These electrons, when they vibrated, gave off electromagnetic radiation, as Lorentz and Zeeman had shown.

Thomson made several other important contributions to atomic physics. However, it was his pupils—and the pupils of his pupils—who went on to solve the next series of atomic puzzles. When J. J. Thomson died, in 1940, at the age of eighty-four, he had had the great satisfaction of living on into an era when man's mastery of the atom was apparently all but complete.

One of Thomson's students at Cambridge was a young man

Ernest Rutherford

from New Zealand who more than any other single individual grasped and penetrated the atomic mystery. To Ernest Rutherford (1871–1937) we owe much of what we know today about the atom.

English settlers had been living on New Zealand's South Island for only a generation when Ernest Rutherford was born there. His grandfather, one of New Zealand's pioneer settlers, had built a sawmill; Rutherford's father, a civil engineer, had experimented with agriculture, developing new and ingenious ways of planting and cultivating flax. Ernest grew up in a large, energetic, active family. The frontier community in which he lived had established a college near his home, and young Rutherford won a scholarship to study there. His work in mathematics was so outstanding that he was given a grant for further study at New Zealand University, and then, in 1895, a scholarship to Cambridge.

These scholarships were awarded to promising students from all over the British Empire, giving them a chance to study at one of England's two great universities. The boys from the colonial outposts often had a hard time getting along with the smooth-mannered, upper-class young men who comprised most of Cambridge's enrollment, but what they lacked in poise and polish they made up in hard work and application.

Rutherford arrived at Cambridge at an exciting moment in the story of atomic physics. Within a few months, Roentgen would discover X rays; two months later, Becquerel was to find his "uranic rays." Soon Madame Curie would be searching for radioactive elements. And, right at Cambridge, J. J. Thomson was near the climax of his work with cathode rays.

Rutherford had been working on the magnetization of iron at New Zealand University. To help him, he had invented a magnetic detector of radio waves. It was an impressive achievement for a twenty-four-year-old student, and J. J. Thomson, who was famous for his clumsiness with experimental apparatus, was particularly impressed by Rutherford's detector. When Rutherford reached Cambridge, Thomson welcomed him and took a special interest in him.

The New Zealander plunged energetically into his studies. One Cambridge scientist said of him, "We've got a rabbit here from the Antipodes and he's burrowing mighty deep." At first, he continued his research into magnetism. But soon he was caught up in the new developments exploding like bombshells in the world of physics.

He helped Thomson, in 1896, with his experiments on cathode-ray tubes. Then Rutherford and Thomson turned to have a look at Roentgen's X rays. In terms of Thomson's ideas, it could now be said that X rays were created through the bombardment of atoms by electrons. When an electric current passed through a vacuum tube, the electrons were hurled against the anode of the tube. As the electrons slammed into the metal of the anode, they somehow jolted the X rays loose. The faster the electrons were traveling as they hit the anode, the more energetic the X rays would be as they flew off. X rays, it now could be seen, were a sort of electromagnetic radiation akin to visible light and the radio waves. Because X rays were so energetic and fast-moving, they had much shorter wavelengths than the other known electromagnetic radiations. (Another way to say that a radiation has a short wavelength is to say that it has a *high frequency*. Look at our diagram of waves again. The wave with longer wavelength has far fewer crests than the other wave. *Frequency* in waves refers to the number of wave crests that go by a given point in a given time. The fewer the crests, the lower the frequency and the greater the wavelength. More crests mean higher frequency and shorter wavelength.)

The high frequency of X rays accounts for their property of penetrating matter. They move so fast that hardly anything is able to halt them. Only heavy elements can stop X rays successfully. Human flesh is made up mostly of light elements like hydrogen, carbon, nitrogen, and oxygen. X rays thus pass easily through flesh. Bone and teeth, though, are built from heavier elements such as calcium and phosphorus, which slow up or stop X rays. Thus an X ray picture shows black

where the X rays get through, gray where they pass with
difficulty, and white where they are stopped altogether.

Rutherford and Thomson showed that X rays were powerful enough to strip electrons away from the atoms of gases
such as air. When an X ray collided with an atom, knocking
out an electron, it left behind a positively charged particle.
Atoms are normally neutral, but an atom that carries an
electrical charge is called an *ion*, from the Greek word meaning "to go." Atoms that have lost electrons, through bombardment by high-enegry particles like X rays, are positive ions.
Atoms that have gained electrons are negative ions. Rutherford and Thomson studied the ionizing power of X rays at just
about the same time that the Curies were measuring the
ionizing power of the rays given off by radioactive uranium.

It was not long before Rutherford found himself studying
those rays too. J. J. Thomson was no longer at his side, though,
for Rutherford had accepted a professorship at McGill University in Montreal. He was only twenty-seven, and the offer to
come to Canada was too tempting for him to pass up. A mil-
lionaire had endowed McGill with one of the finest physics
laboratories in the world. Late in 1898, Rutherford sailed
westward to begin his new career.

He ordered compounds of uranium and thorium at once,
set up a research department, and started to search for an
explanation of the radiation given off by the radioactive substances. Pierre Curie and other experimenters were able to
show, by 1900, that the rays emanating from radium included
particles carrying an electrical charge. They were probably
electrons, Curie thought. Rutherford thought so, too—but he
suspected that radioactivity involved more than one kind of
ray.

He put some radium into a hollow piece of lead in which

a hole had been bored. The lead blocked the rays from escaping except through the hole. Rutherford then put his piece of lead between the poles of a powerful magnet.

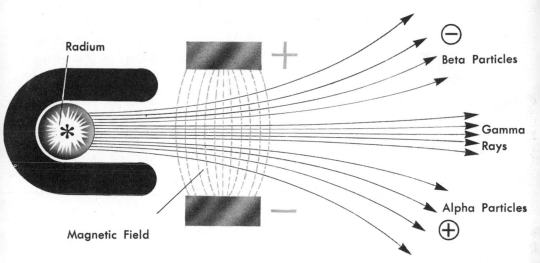

Rutherford's Three Kinds of Radioactive Rays

He discovered that the beam of radiation from the radium was split in three. One branch of the beam went off toward the positive pole of the magnet. One branch headed toward the negative pole. The third branch continued straight ahead, unaffected by the magnetic field.

Rutherford saw that three rays were involved. The rays that were deflected toward the positive pole were the lightest, since they "bent" much more than the others. Rutherford gave these rays the name of *beta rays*, from the second letter of the Greek alphabet. They bore a negative charge, and seemed much like a beam of electrons, except that they moved at a much greater speed than the electrons Thomson had measured moving through vacuum tubes. We now know that the beta rays (now called "beta particles") are indeed fast-moving electrons flung out by radioactive atoms.

The positively charged rays Rutherford called *alpha rays* ("alpha particles" today). They moved much less rapidly than the beta rays. Rutherford was able to calculate that each alpha particle carried a double positive charge, and that the alpha particles were bulky, with a mass about 7,000 times that of an electron.

The third type of rays was given the name of *gamma rays*. A French physicist named Paul Villard was the first to discover them. The gamma rays were fast-moving and extremely penetrating. We know now that while alpha particles and beta patricles are fragments of atoms, gamma rays are electromagnetic radiations of short wavelength and high frequency, resembling X rays in most respects.

Rays and more rays! By 1902, Rutherford and a fellow scientist, Frederick Soddy, offered an explanation of radioactivity that took into account these new types of rays, the three types that now were known to make up the old "uranic rays" of Becquerel.

Not all elements, Rutherford and Soddy said, were stable for all eternity. Some of the very heavy elements like radium, polonium, thorium, and uranium tended to break down spontaneously. Though Rutherford and his colleagues could not say why it happened, these heavy elements had a tendency to shoot particles out of themselves and thus disintegrate.

As the radioactive elements threw off their particles, Rutherford went on, they underwent great alterations. When an atom of uranium gave off particles, it broke down by a series of stages into the somewhat lighter element radium. The decay did not end there, because radium was unstable also and gave off radioactive particles itself. So the breakdown continued until the radium had changed into lead. Lead, not being radioactive, was the end product of the series.

This meant that the particles given off had to have considerable weight. Uranium, it was known, had an atomic weight of 238. Lead's atomic weight was 206. The process whereby an atom of uranium changed to an atom of lead involved the loss of the equivalent weight of about 32 atoms of hydrogen.

Rutherford sought to prove this experimentally. It took him three years to do it. Using radium as his particle source, he trapped alpha particles in a glass tube and analyzed them with a spectroscope. He discovered that the tube was full of helium atoms!

What had happened? Where had the helium come from?

Rutherford deduced the answer. The alpha particles that entered the tube, he said, were helium ions. Helium has an atomic weight of 4; a helium ion, stripped of its electrons, still has just about the same atomic weight, since electrons are so small they have practically no weight even compared with atoms. Entering the glass tube, the alpha particles, with their double positive charge, attracted two electrons apiece and combined with them. The result was that they turned back into helium atoms.

It was a novel and bewildering idea in 1904. But it had the advantage of logic. Rutherford had measured alpha particles and knew that their atomic weight was just about the same as that of atoms of helium. And his spectroscope had detected helium atoms in the glass tube where he had trapped alpha particles. He knew, too, that each alpha particle carried a double positive electrical charge. That had been determined with the help of a young German physicist, Hans Geiger, who had invented a device for counting ionized particles. When an ionizing particle passed through the gas in the Geiger counter, electrical sparks were touched off that could be counted and photographed. The counter provided a record of the number of alpha particles entering it, and from that the electrical charge of each particle could be computed.

So the alpha particle, bursting out of a radioactive atom, was simply a helium ion. Passing through a gas, it ripped electrons from gas atoms, thus ionizing them. With each collision, the fast-moving alpha particle lost a little of its energy, until finally it slowed down enough to combine with two loose electrons and become a helium atom.

Radioactive atoms gave off helium, then! How strange that seemed! It was possible now to work out so-called "radioactive series" showing how the radioactive elements broke down into lead. The breakdown of uranium, for instance, involved the discharge by each uranium atom of eight alpha particles. The total atomic weight lost was $8 \times 4 = 32$, which accounted for uranium's whole loss while breaking down from its weight of 238 to lead's 206. (The gamma rays and beta particles also given off by uranium during the series had no weight worth speaking of; though, as we will see, that does not mean they were unimportant in the process.)

By 1904, then, Rutherford had explained a great deal of what went on during radioactive decay. He had shown a startled world that one element could change of its own accord into another. The atom, once thought indivisible, divided itself into smaller particles. Out of the once-thought-eternal atom there could come helium ions, electrons, and high-energy electromagnetic radiation.

The best description of radioactivity that I have ever seen was written in 1934 by Sir James Jeans, the English physicist. Jeans wrote:

"The break-up of a radioactive atom may be compared to the discharge of a gun; the alpha particle is the shot fired, the beta particles are the smoke, and the gamma rays are the flash. The atom of lead which finally remains is the unloaded gun, and the original radioactive atom, of uranium or what not, was the loaded gun."

The unusual thing about such radioactive "guns," Jeans noted, was "that they go off spontaneously and of their own accord. All attempts to pull the trigger have so far failed. . . ."

Today we know how to pull that trigger and make the radioactive "gun" go off whenever we want it to. The discovery was accomplished less than a decade after Sir James Jeans wrote those lines—but discussion of how it was done will have to wait.

At the beginning of this century, it was enough simply to know that such "guns" existed and that they might go off at any time. But how frequently did such atomic triggerings happen? Was there any way to predict them?

There was, and the concept of "half-life" was invented to explain the rate of radioactive decay. Rutherford and other experimenters found that the different radioactive elements broke down at very different rates. It was impossible to predict when any given atom of uranium or thorium or radium might suddenly go haywire and throw off radioactive particles. But it turned out to be possible to predict the *probability* of a radioactive discharge among a large group of atoms of the same substance.

For instance, if you take a single atom of radium, you have no way of knowing how long it will last before breakdown. It might disintegrate a second from now, or next October, or 50,000 years hence. But if you take a million atoms of radium, it becomes possible to calculate the chances of a breakdown within the group.

In any million atoms of radium, half will disintegrate in the next 1,580 years. Of the half million remaining after that time, another half will disintegrate in the next 1,580 years. A quarter of a million will remain, but half of these will break down in another 1,580 years, and so on and on until there are only a few thousand atoms left, and then a few hundred, and then a few dozen.

It is the same for every radioactive element, but the half-lives are different. The half-life of the heaviest naturally occurring radioactive element, uranium, is 4.5 billion years. So in any quantity of uranium, half will be left after that time, a quarter left after 9 billion years, an eighth left after 13.5 billion years, a sixteenth left after 18 billion years, and so on. At the other extreme, the half-life of the element radon is only 4 days. The half-life of a certain type of radium is just a millionth of a second. The half-life of polonium is 3 minutes.

It may seem as though something is wrong here. If polonium has a half-life of only 3 minutes, how could Madame Curie have found any in her ton of pitchblende? With such a brief half-life, it would seem that all the polonium in the world must have disintegrated billions of years ago.

True enough. An hour or so after the creation of the world, all the original polonium had broken down into lead. But radioactive breakdown involves an endless series. Long-lived uranium, when it disintegrates, gives off an alpha particle and becomes thorium. Eventually the thorium atom does the same and breaks down into a still lighter element. On its path through the radioactive series toward its end product of lead, the atom for a while becomes polonium. Thus, new polonium is always being formed by the radioactive decay of heavier elements. The same is true of the other short-lived radioactive elements found in the world today. They were not there at the creation of the world; they are formed along the way by radioactivity.

Rutherford also found that the decaying atoms gave off energy when they broke down. The alpha particles came flying out at a great speed. Obviously, if an atom of radium or uranium could give such a powerful "kick" to such heavy particles, a colossal quantity of energy was locked up within the tiny atom. Could that energy somehow be liberated and harnessed for the use of man? That must have seemed the wildest of wild dreams in 1904!

In his first few years at McGill, Rutherford had performed wonders. He had identified the components that made up Becquerel's "uranic rays." He had shown that elements could change into other elements. He had captured single atoms— the helium atoms produced by the combination of alpha particles and electrons—for the first time. By the time he returned to England in the spring of 1907, to take a professorship at the University of Manchester, Rutherford had done enough to win him undying fame in the history of science. In 1908 he received the Nobel Prize in Chemistry, in recognition of his investigations into the decay of elements and the chemistry of radioactive substances. King Edward VII of Great Britain knighted him soon after, making him Sir Ernest Rutherford.

Such honors often come at the climax of a man's life, when he has accomplished all he is ever going to accomplish. Sir Ernest, though, was only on the threshold of his biggest triumphs. He turned to a field of research that would have seemed beyond man's reach only a dozen years earlier. It was now clear that the atom, far from being the ultimate "building block" of matter, was itself made up of smaller units.

Rutherford sought to find out what atoms were made of.

5

THE HEART OF THE ATOM

What was the inside of an atom like, Rutherford asked?

There were many theories, now that Dalton's old billiard-ball idea was dead. One suggestion came from Philipp Lenard, whose vacuum tube Roentgen had used in the discovery of X rays. Lenard, making cathode-ray experiments of his own, had seen how easily the rays passed through aluminum foil. It occurred to him that the atoms of aluminum must consist mostly of empty space, so that rays could pass right through without interference. Lenard thought that the atom might contain tiny centers of force that he called "dynamids," each made up of an electron and some positive charge close together. Between these dynamids was just emptiness.

J. J. Thomson had a different concept. To him, the atom was a sphere of positive electrification, with electrons embedded in it like raisins in a cake. In Thomson's model of the atom, the electrons were arranged in rings rotating around the center of the atom. He computed that the inner ring could hold only 5 electrons; atoms with 6 or more electrons needed a second ring, which could hold 16 electrons, and so on. An atom with 70 electrons, Thomson figured, would need 6 concentric rings.

There was much merit in Thomson's raisins-in-a-cake picture. It had a fatal flaw, though. According to the laws of physics as they were then understood, a moving electric charge would give off electromagnetic waves and thus lose energy. As the electrons became weaker, their orbits would grow smaller, until finally they would all tumble into the center of the atom. This seemed to rule out any arrangement of electrons in moving rings. The problem continued to bewilder scientists for many years, until, as we shall see, a bold new explanation got around the whole problem.

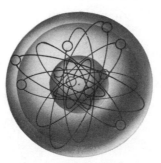

Thomson's Model of the Atom

Rutherford, like many others, was eager to discover the structure of the atom, now that it was known to contain electrons (and thus also some kind of positive charges.) Rutherford liked Lenard's idea that the atom was mostly empty space, and did not agree with Thomson's raisin-cake parallel. He sought for some experimental method for peering into the heart of the atom.

In 1906, while studying the behavior of alpha particles, Rutherford had noticed that the particles tended to change direction slightly when they passed through a thin sheet of mica. A couple of years later, Hans Geiger followed this observation up by discovering that thin films of gold deflected alpha particles even more. Rutherford and Geiger, along with Rutherford's student Ernest Marsden, used this discovery in their quest.

Their method has been compared to the way a customs officer might look for weapons hidden in bales of cotton. If he fired his gun at a bale containing just cotton, the bullet would either go straight through or else get stuck in the cotton. But if guns happen to be hidden in the bale, the bullet, striking them, would bounce off at a strange angle.

Rutherford went shooting at atoms—with alpha particles for his bullets!

He inserted some radium in a block of lead, leaving a hole through which alpha particles could exit. As his target, he

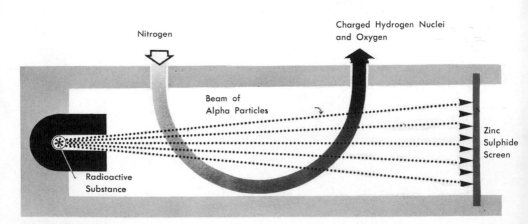

Rutherford's Nitrogen Bombardments

used small screens coated with zinc sulphide. Alpha particles, striking the screens, would give off bright flashes of light.

Then he took a thin piece of gold foil and put it between his alpha particle "gun" and the screens. The foil, thin as it was, was several thousand atoms thick—theoretically enough to stop alpha particles.

Rutherford fired a stream of alpha particles at the gold foil. The screens continued to light up—so the alpha particles were passing right through the atoms of gold! It was the final proof that the atom could not possibly be a solid ball. Some of the particles that went through were turned slightly aside, as though they had glancingly struck against something on their way through the foil. Other alpha particles were deflected at wide angles. And—astonishingly—some of the alpha particles came bouncing right back toward the radium source!

"It was quite the most incredible event that ever happened to me in my life," Rutherford said later. "It was almost as incredible as if you had fired a 15-inch shell at a piece of tissue paper and it came back and hit you."

The atoms of gold in the foil evidently were mostly empty space, as Lenard had suggested years before. So most of the alpha particles had simply passed right through as if nothing stood in their way. A few, though—perhaps one out of every 8,000 particles—had collided with something small but massive within the gold atoms. Those particles had been deflected or even bounced right back.

Rutherford published his work in May, 1911, in a history-making paper called "The Scattering of Alpha and Beta Particles by Matter and the Structure of the Atom." He explained his findings by conceiving a new model of the atom. His model showed the atom composed of a central charge, surrounded by a sphere of electrification of equal but opposite charge. At first, Rutherford had no idea whether the central charge was positive or negative. "For convenience," he wrote, "the sign will be assumed positive."

Rutherford's Model of the Atom

Soon, though, he had determined that the central core—which he now called the *nucleus* of the atom—was indeed positive. Around it was a cloud of negative charges, electrons. Practically all the atom's mass was in the nucleus. Electrons were so tiny that they had almost no mass and took up almost no space, so that most of the atom was indeed empty. As Sir James Jeans put it, "It is as useless to discuss how much room an electron takes up as to discuss how much room a fear, an anxiety, or an uncertainty takes up."

The greater the nucleus of an atom, the greater its atomic weight, Rutherford insisted. Hydrogen, the lightest element, had the smallest nucleus. Uranium, the heaviest, had the most massive nucleus. Around this nucleus, the electrons of an atom moved in much the same way that planets did around the sun of a solar system.

The alpha particle, he now saw clearly, was the nucleus of a helium atom—a helium atom minus its two electrons. It seemed likely to Rutherford that, since radioactive atoms threw off helium nuclei, the alpha particle was one of the basic building blocks of the nucleus. It was also probable, he felt, that the hydrogen nucleus, the simplest of all atomic cores, was such a basic building block. "No doubt," he wrote, "the positively charged center of the atom [the nucleus] is a complicated system in movement, consisting in part of charged helium and hydrogen atoms."

This suggestion raised an immediate objection. How could a nucleus be made up of positively charged particles? According to the classical laws of physics, particles with the same charge would tend to repel each other, not cling together. Rutherford himself was aware of this difficulty. He wrote, "It would appear as if the positively charged atoms of matter attract one another at very small distances, for otherwise it is difficult to see how the component parts at the center are held together." Today, more than half a century after Rutherford wrote those words, physicists are still puzzling over the problem of what holds the nucleus together.

Rutherford's discovery of the atomic nucleus earned him no headlines in 1911. Atoms were remote, fantastic things to the ordinary man then. Even Rutherford's fellow scientists generally failed to recognize the importance of his discovery. They thought, at first, that it was just another of the many theoretical models of the atom that were being suggested. They did not realize that he had hit on something basic to all further understanding of the atom.

A few men, though, seized at once on Rutherford's work and carried it onward. Rutherford had by no means solved all the mysteries of the atom's structure. He had only begun to clear away the fog of ignorance.

No one yet knew how the "cloud" of electrons was arranged

around the nucleus. Nor was there yet any definite under-standing of what the nucleus itself was composed of. But there came to Rutherford's laboratory at Manchester, in the spring of 1912, an energetic, high-spirited Dane named Niels Bohr who not only improved on Rutherford's knowledge of the atomic nucleus, but stood all of classical physics on its head to show how the electrons in the outer structure of the atom were arranged.

Niels Bohr (1885–1962) was a towering figure in atomic physics for most of this century. His great career spanned both theoretical and practical physics, since he not only helped to explain the structure of the atom, but many years later took part in the grim research that produced the atomic bomb.

He was the eldest of three children. He studied physics in Denmark's one university of that time, the University of Copenhagen, and took a master's degree in physics in 1909. Two years later he received his doctorate. Then the Carlsberg Foundation, established by a famous beer company of Den-mark, gave him a grant for study abroad.

The best place for a young physicist to study in 1912 was England, and the best man to study with was Rutherford. Bohr spent only a few months at Rutherford's laboratory, but he did heroic work in that short span.

Bohr's most important contributions dealt with the role of the electrons, and we will get to that topic shortly. His theory of the atomic nucleus adopted Rutherford's idea that the nucleus had a positive charge. In the case of hydrogen, Bohr said, there was a single positive charge in the nucleus, and a single electron whirling in an orbit around it. The two charges balanced each other out, since atoms are electrically neutral.

Helium, the next heaviest element, had two positive charges in the nucleus, and two electrons. When a helium atom was ionized, an alpha particle remained—simply the double positive charge already mentioned.

A Dutch physicist, Antonius van den Broek, carried Bohr's thinking a little further. He suggested that there was a rising series of positive charges right through the periodic table. By now, almost 90 elements were known, and, counting the blanks, there were 92 spaces in the periodic table from hydrogen to uranium. Van den Broek argued that each atom had a positive nuclear charge equal to its place in the table—radium, number 88 in the table, had a positive charge 88 times that of hydrogen, 44 times that of helium, and so on.

Bohr's Model of the Atom

Meanwhile, several other physicists were working out the law that governs the changes in an element's place in the periodic table due to radioactivity. Under this formula, a radioactive element that gives off an alpha particle drops two places in the table, because an alpha particle consists of two positive charges. So when uranium, with its 92 positive charges, gives off an alpha particle, it becomes thorium, a 90-charge atom. On the other hand, when a radioactive atom emits a beta particle, it *gains* one place in the table. This happens because giving off a beta particle, with its one negative charge, amounts to the same thing as gaining one positive charge. So when thorium, element 90, gives off a beta particle, it becomes protactinium, element 91.

The work of van den Broek received its final polishing at the hands of a brilliant young Englishman named H. G. J. Moseley. Moseley carried out experiments with X rays that went far beyond Roentgen's. Roentgen had used platinum anodes as his target for producing X rays. Moseley systematically used 42 different elements as the targets for the electron bombardment that produces X rays. He analyzed the waves each element produced, and discovered that, as the experiment proceeded up the table of atomic weights, the frequency of the X rays produced increased in exact proportion.

Moseley concluded from this that "we have here a proof that there is in the atom a fundamental quantity, which increases by regular steps as we go from one element to the next. The quantity can only be the charge on the central positive nucleus."

He gave this positive charge the name of *atomic number*. Hydrogen's atomic number is 1. Helium's is 2. Lithium's is 3. And so on up the scale of elements to uranium, 92. The atomic number of an element is equal to the number of positive charges it carries in its nucleus. The atomic *number* should never be confused with the atomic *weight*, which is the total relative weight of the atom. Oxygen, for instance, has the atomic number 8, but an atomic weight of about 16. Gold, atomic number 79, has an atomic weight of about 197.

If the nucleus of the atom, with its positive charge, contains most of the atom's mass, why does the atomic weight exceed the atomic number so greatly? Since electrons have almost no mass, what else is there in the atom that provides the missing weight? When Moseley performed his experiments, no one knew the answer to that—and it remained a mystery for almost twenty years.

Moseley himself did not get a chance to solve that mystery. He carried his experiments along only to element 79, gold, and then was called away to serve in Britain's army during World War I. For all his scientific brilliance, he was simply sent out to the front line as an ordinary soldier, and there he died in battle in August, 1915, at the age of 27.

The war also kept Sir Ernest Rutherford busy—not in the trenches, but in his laboratory. He spent the war years working on instruments to detect submarines. Not until late in 1917 was he free to return to the quest for atomic knowledge.

He sought now to understand the atomic nucleus—and he thought he could best do this by splitting it. While in the United States just before the outbreak of World War I, Rutherford had said, "It is possible that the nucleus of an atom may be altered by the direct collision of the nucleus with atoms of helium such as are ejected from radioactive matter." Now he set up apparatus to see if this were so.

Once again, Rutherford used alpha particles as his bullets. He bombarded nitrogen gas with alpha particles, setting up a zinc sulphide screen to record the flashes of any charged particles that might be given off. He knew that alpha particles could not travel more than a very short distance from his experiment. His screens, set up beyond the range of alpha particles, nevertheless showed flashes of light. Some other particle was being produced by the collision of nitrogen atoms and alpha particles.

Rutherford wrote, "It is difficult to avoid the conclusion that these long-range atoms arising from the collision of alpha particles with nitrogen . . . are probably charged atoms of hydrogen."

He went on to conclude that the hydrogen nucleus was the

basic positive charge from which all atoms were constructed. Since hydrogen was the simplest atom, and its nucleus had only one positive charge, this followed logically. Rutherford gave the ionized hydrogen atom the name of *proton*, from a Greek word meaning "the first one" or "the most important." The nuclei of atoms, he said, were made up of combinations of protons.

It still remained to "catch" a proton and identify it. This was accomplished in 1925 by the English physicist P. M. S. Blackett, who repeated Rutherford's experiment and succeeded in taking photographs of protons.

This seemingly fantastic accomplishment was made possible by an invention of C. T. R. Wilson, one of J. J. Thomson's pupils at Cambridge. Wilson, the son of a Scottish farmer, was born in 1869, and while still in his teens carried out valuable studies on cloud formation at an observatory atop Scotland's highest mountain, Ben Nevis. In 1888 he went to Cambridge, where he continued his studies of clouds and atmospheric electricity, and measured the natural radioactivity of rain and snow. He had remarkable skill in constructing experimental equipment, and that was a talent that never failed to awe the mechanically inept J. J. Thomson.

One day Thomson called Wilson in and said, "Can you help me photograph an electron?" It seemed like an incredible request, but Wilson took it seriously and set out to build apparatus that would do just that. The result—after many years of work—was the Wilson cloud chamber, which he completed in 1911.

The cloud chamber is a box with a glass window at the top, mica windows at the sides, and a movable piston at the bottom. Through one of the side windows, air saturated with water vapor is let into the box. Then the piston is suddenly pulled down, causing the air to expand and cool. The water vapor condenses and turns to fog.

An experimenter next shoots charged particles into the chamber through one of the mica windows. As the particles pass through the fog, they ionize its atoms. Fog tends to collect around ions in the air, and so the track of the charged particles shows up as a heavy streak of fog against the thinner background fog of the cloud chamber. This can be seen with the naked eye, and it can be photographed. Thus, while it was obviously impossible to see or photograph such tiny particles as electrons or protons, it became quite possible to photograph the tracks they left behind as they flashed through the fog of the cloud chamber.

Thomson used the cloud chamber to photograph the tracks of electrons. Later, Rutherford made use of it to study alpha particles. The cloud chamber became an indispensable tool of the atomic physicist, and Wilson was honored by a Nobel prize in 1927 for its development. It remained standard equipment in laboratories until quite recently, when more sophisticated devices largely replaced it.

Blackett, in 1925, used the cloud chamber to photograph the collision between alpha particles and nitrogen atoms. Since ordinary air is more than 70% nitrogen, all Blackett had to do was shoot alpha particles through an air-filled cloud chamber and photograph the action. He worked for nearly 6 months, firing 415,000 alpha particles through the cloud chamber and taking 23,000 pictures. After painstakingly examining these thousands of photographs, he found just eight that showed alpha particles hitting the nuclei of nitrogen atoms.

These few photographs showed the alpha particle rocketing straight toward a nitrogen atom. At the point of impact, the track of the alpha particle kinked and thickened as the particle smashed into and joined with the nitrogen nucleus. The track of another, lighter particle could be seen shooting off at an angle.

This light particle was Rutherford's proton, Blackett showed. Only about a fourth as massive as an alpha particle, it was about 1,840 times as heavy as an electron. However, it carried an electrical charge equal to but opposite that of an electron.

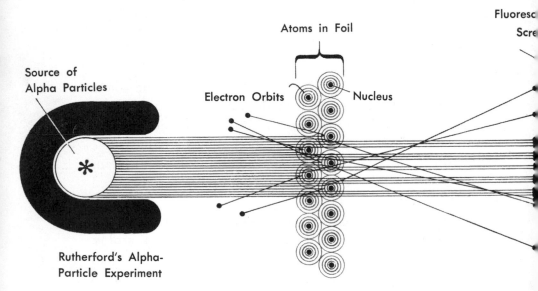

Finding the proton was not the only important result of this experiment. Blackett also proved that Rutherford, in 1919, had achieved the alchemists' dream: he had succeeded in changing one element into another in the laboratory!

The nitrogen atom had an atomic number of 7, meaning

that its nucleus contained seven protons. The alpha particle, which was, of course, simply a helium nucleus, consisted of two protons. When Rutherford sent the alpha particle smashing into the nitrogen nucleus, he was putting nine protons together for a brief moment. The collision, though, sent one proton—which is to say a single hydrogen nucleus—flying loose.

That still left eight protons joined together. The atom whose nucleus has eight protons is oxygen. Rutherford had turned nitrogen into oxygen and hydrogen by bombarding it with alpha particles! For the first time, men had broken and changed the atomic nucleus.

Other experiments in "alchemy" followed. The English scientists bombarded many light elements with alpha particles, and were able to turn boron into carbon, sodium into magnesium, aluminum into silicon, and phosphorus into sulfur. Of course, incredibly small amounts of these elements were transmuted—a handful of atoms at best. But it was a beginning.

It was now established that the atomic nucleus contained the small but heavy positive charges called protons, and that an equal number of negatively charged electrons circled the nucleus in some sort of orbit, giving the atom as a whole a neutral electrical charge. Atomic knowledge had come a long way in the first two decades of this century. But much was still unexplained.

How was it that the electrons, with their negative charge, did not fly straight into the nucleus, attracted by the positive protons? And how could the moving electrons continue to give off the energy of electromagnetic radiation without losing any energy themselves? The puzzles of the electrons were disturbing ones.

And the nucleus held puzzles, too. Why was there such a

difference between atomic number and atomic weight? A radium atom, for instance, contained 88 protons, each with the weight of a hydrogen nucleus, and 88 electrons, with practically no weight at all. Thus the atomic weight of radium ought to be a little more than 88 at most. But it was actually about 226. Where did the extra weight come from?

The most popular theory just after World War I said that there had to be extra protons in the nucleus, electrically balanced by extra electrons. The radium atom, according to this theory, really had 226 protons in its nucleus, and 138 electrons. This gave the nucleus a positive charge of $+88$, which was balanced by the 88 electrons in orbit around the nucleus. It was an ingenious idea, and it was almost right. Almost—but not quite.

A new problem appeared when it was discovered that the same element might have several atomic weights. By the time the answer was found, the question of the structure of the nucleus was no longer such a puzzler.

It had always seemed odd that atoms could have atomic weights that were not whole numbers. The hydrogen atom had a weight of 1; it was the building block on which all other atomic weights were originally figured. Chlorine, for example, has an atomic weight of 35.46. According to the current theory of the time, a chlorine atom contained 35 protons. The electrons it contained had a total mass of 35/1840. Where did the other weight come from? Could there be a fraction of a proton in the nucleus? Almost all the other atoms, too, had atomic weights that were not whole numbers.

As early as 1886, Sir William Crookes—he of the Crookes tube—had made a startling suggestion. "Probably," he wrote, "our atomic weights merely represent a mean value around which the actual atomic weights of the atoms vary within certain narrow limits. . . . I conceive, therefore, that when we say the atomic weight of, for instance, calcium is 40, we really express the fact that, while the majority of calcium atoms have an actual atomic weight 40, there are not a few which are represented by 39 or 41, a less number by 38 or 42, and so on."

In 1912, J. J. Thomson had been experimenting with neon gas, subjecting it to magnetic and electric fields in the hope of finding the positive particles of its atom. He did not succeed in this—the proton would not be discovered for seven years—but he did uncover something unusual. Neon's atomic weight, he knew, was 20.18. But when he applied a magnetic field to a vacuum tube through which charged neon particles were passing, they separated into two streams, one with an atomic weight of 20, the other with an atomic weight of 22. Was neon really a mixture of two elements, Thomson wondered? That was hardly possible. But then there must be two kinds of neon, with identical chemical properties but different weights. That, too, seemed very strange.

Another of Thomson's Cambridge pupils, F. W. Aston (1877–1945) concentrated on the problem. Aston tried to separate the two kinds of neon by using a clay barrier, but had little luck. In 1919, he invented a magnetic separating device, known today as the *mass spectrograph*, with which he was more successful. Aston's machine sent charged atoms at high speeds, through magnetic and electric fields. These fields deflected the atoms according to their weight as they headed for a photographic plate. The heaviest atoms would land at a particular place on the photographic plate, the next heaviest would land alongside them, the next heaviest next to them, and so on. Aston could also measure the relative amounts of the atoms in each weight group by seeing how dark a line they made on the photographic plate.

When he tried it with neon, he confirmed Thomson's findings. Neon actually consisted of two types, with atomic weights of 20 and 22. The lighter gas was ten times as abundant as the heavier one. That was why neon's accepted atomic weight had been 20.18. The figure actually represented an *average* of the atomic weights of the two kinds of neon, which were always mixed in the same proportion in nature.

Frederick Soddy, Rutherford's old colleague in the early radioactivity experiments, coined the word *isotopes*, from the Greek for "same place," to refer to the different types of the same element. Isotopes had the same chemical properties but different atomic weights. The existence of isotopes was explained by saying that some atoms had more proton–electron pairs in their nuclei than others of the same element, thus having a greater atomic weight while still keeping the same positive charge on the nucleus. As we will soon see, that theory gave way to a better one.

Aston turned next to chlorine, with its atomic weight of 35.46. He found that chlorine consisted of two isotopes, one with an atomic weight of 37, the other of 35. By the end of 1920, Aston had examined 19 elements and found that 9 had isotopes. For this work, he was given the 1922 Nobel Prize for Chemistry. Meanwhile, in the United States, the physicist A. J. Dempster had independently invented a mass spectrograph even more efficient than Aston's, and had found isotopes of lithium, magnesium, potassium, calcium, and zinc.

Today we know of hundreds of isotopes. Some elements have only one or two. Tin, on the other hand, has 10, with atomic weights ranging from 112 to 124. With the discovery of isotopes, it was no longer possible to talk about an atom of tin or neon or any other element without identifying it by weight.

Physicists use the *mass number* to identify atoms. The mass number is the atomic weight of a given isotope rounded off to the nearest whole number. Thus hydrogen's lightest istotope has an atomic weight of 1.00797. Its mass number is 1. Oxygen has three isotopes, with exact atomic weights like 15.9994 and 17.00453. For convenience, they are referred to by their mass numbers—oxygen-16, oxygen-17, oxygen-18. So there are three ways of naming atoms: by their atomic number (the number of positive charges in the nucleus), their atomic weight (the weight of the atom relative to the weight of an atom of carbon-12), and their mass number (the atomic weight of a given isotope, rounded to a whole number). When atomic weights are given on a periodic table, they refer to the average weight of all the naturally occurring isotopes of an element. But in the laboratory the atomic weight of each isotope is calculated to many decimal places.

Aston, the "isotope hunter," had added one more clue to the nature of the atom. A given element might be of several types. The explanation of the isotope arrangement, though, was not completely satisfactory. Rutherford and his colleagues were not happy with the idea that the extra weight resulted from the presence of extra proton–electron combinations in the nucleus.

In 1920, an American scientist named William D. Harkins suggested that the extra protons and electrons that supposedly were in the nucleus might actually join together to form a single particle. He gave the name *neutron* to this particle, which would have mass but no electrical charge.

Such a particle would account for certain troublesome arithmetical problems. Why, for instance, did an alpha particle have twice the charge of the proton, but four times the mass? Could it be that alpha particles really consisted of two protons and two neutrons? It was twelve years before that question was answered.

The answer came from Rutherford's laboratory. In 1918, Rutherford had returned to Cambridge, taking J. J. Thomson's Cavendish Professorship when Thomson accepted a higher post in Trinity College. Many brilliant physicists clustered around Rutherford at Cambridge like electrons around a nucleus. Among them was James Chadwick, born in Manchester in 1891. Chadwick had studied with Rutherford when they were both at the University of Manchester just before World War I. In 1913, Chadwick went to Berlin to confer with another Rutherford assistant, Hans Geiger. "I was in the middle of the experiments on beta rays when the war broke out," Chadwick wrote to Rutherford. He was forced to remain in Germany until the end of the war. While a prisoner, he was allowed to carry out experiments in radioactivity.

After the war, Chadwick joined Rutherford at Cambridge, and took part in the 1919 experiments that split the nucleus of nitrogen. In 1923, Chadwick told Rutherford, "I think we shall have to make a real search for the neutron. I believe I have a scheme which may just work, but I must consult Aston first."

The neutron eluded Chadwick for almost a decade. In 1932, he conducted some experiments based on work done two years earlier by a pair of Germans, Walther Bothe and H. Becker. Bothe and Becker had found that when the alpha particles from polonium struck the light element beryllium, a ray of great penetrating power was given off. This ray was unaffected by any electric or magnetic field.

Chadwick repeated the German experiments. He showed that the new rays could not be electromagnetic radiation such as gamma rays or X rays. They moved too slowly for that— only about a tenth as fast as gamma rays. Chadwick suspected that the new rays might consist of particles.

He sent a beam of the rays through a cloud chamber filled with nitrogen. The photographs he took showed the nitrogen nuclei being buffeted around, as though by collision with some kind of atomic particle. But the penetrating radiation left no track through the cloud chamber. That meant it had no electric charge; it traversed the chamber without ionizing the vapor. Yet it was big enough to knock sturdy nitrogen nuclei about, and even to jolt protons loose from them!

He realized that the new radiation consisted of a stream of electrically neutral particles of fairly heavy mass—Harkins' long-sought neutrons. Because they had no charge, the neutrons left no trail of ionized vapor across the cloud chamber. But they had as much mass as protons—in fact, later experiments showed that neutrons were very slightly heavier than protons.

The discovery of the neutron completed the basic picture of the nucleus. The nucleus consists of protons and neutrons, bound together by some unknown force that even today is a matter for speculation. Every element has its own individual quota of protons in the nucleus. Nitrogen and no other element has 7 protons; silver and no other element has 47 protons; uranium and no other element, 92 protons.

Isotopes result from differing quantities of neutrons in the nucleus. Every atom of tin has 50 protons, for instance. But some tin atoms have 62 neutrons, some have 64, some 66, and so on up to 74 neutrons. The presence of more neutrons changes the atomic weight of the atom, but not its chemical properties.

Thus there can be several elements whose isotopes have the same mass number. There is an isotope of carbon with the mass number 14, and an isotope of nitrogen whose mass number is also 14. But carbon-14 is carbon, and nitrogen-14 is nitrogen. The carbon atom has 6 protons and 8 neutrons;

the nitrogen atom has 7 protons and 7 neutrons. The number of protons, not the mass number, determines the element.

Experiment has shown that most of an atom's mass—99.95% of it, in fact—is concentrated in the nucleus. But, though atoms themselves are tiny, the nucleus is almost infinitely tiny. The hydrogen atom is about one two-hundred-fifty-millionth of an inch in diameter. The uranium atom, at the other end of the periodic table, is two and a half times as large. So small is the uranium nucleus, though, that 7,000 of them could be stretched side by side along the diameter of a single uranium atom.

That means that protons and neutrons must be far smaller than the uranium nucleus, since there are about 238 neutrons and protons in that atom. It works out that the electron has a diameter of about one twenty-five-trillionth (1/25,000,000,-000,000) of an inch. The proton, though it is roughly 1,840 times as heavy as the electron, has only one eighteen-hundredth the diameter. Its diameter has been estimated at one forty-five-quadrillionth of an inch. The neutron is about the size of the proton.

The world of the atom is a world of the incredibly small. And—as physicists found out, to their surprise and bewilderment, the rules of that incredibly small world differ from the rules of our world. To explain the atom, it was necessary to create a brand-new theory of physics.

6

WAVES OR PARTICLES?

Between 1911 and 1932, Rutherford, Aston, Soddy, Chadwick, and others did much to explain the structure of the atomic nucleus. When physicists tried to explain the arrangement of the electrons around the nucleus, though, they ran into serious problems. To understand how they coped with these difficulties, we have to go back a bit.

In 1873 James Clerk Maxwell proved mathematically that electricity, magnetism, and light all were related phenomena. Soon, Hertz found the very long, low-frequency electromagnetic waves that bear his name, and Roentgen had discovered the high-frequency X rays at the other end of the electromagnetic spectrum.

Meanwhile, Lorentz and Zeeman in the Netherlands had demonstrated that electromagnetic waves—including light, of course—are created by the vibration of electrons in the atoms of matter. The colors of light are caused by electrons vibrating at different frequencies. As the electrons become more agitated, the radiation they give off increases in frequency—in other words, the wavelength becomes shorter—and the color emitted moves up the visible spectrum from the red or low-frequency end to the violet or high-frequency end. This explains the changes in color of a bar of metal in a furnace. As it grows hotter, its color changes from red to orange to yellow. This happens because the electrons vibrate more intensely under greater heat, and the wavelength of the emitted radiation gets shorter.

Classical physics had predicted that some energy would be given off at every possible frequency by a heated body. Investigation showed, though, that this was not true. There were gaps, certain frequencies at which no energy was given off. Where did the error lie?

A German physicist named Max Planck (1858–1947) supplied an answer in 1900. The classical theory was wrong, he said. Energy radiation was not continuous. Instead, the energy was emitted in the form of little bundles or packets which he called "energy elements." In 1905, Albert Einstein suggested the name *quanta* for the "energy elements," from the Latin word *quantum*, meaning "how much." Planck's theory became known as the *quantum theory*, and it eventually altered all of physics.

According to the classical theory, a vibrating electron might have any value of energy. That is to say, it might give off electromagnetic radiation anywhere up and down the scale. Planck replaced this with the idea that any resonating body— that is, any vibrating electron—must always be at one place and one place only along the scale. It could not change the frequency of the radiation it emitted unless some force acted upon it to make it change.

Under the old theory, we might visualize a continuous ramp with an electron moving along it. At the bottom end of the ramp, the electron gives off radiation of low frequency; as it moves toward the upper end of the ramp, the frequency emitted gets higher. At any given moment the electron might be anywhere along the ramp.

Planck replaced this image with one of a ladder. A resonator, he said, must always be on one particular rung. To reach a different rung, it has to "jump." Jumping to a higher rung could be accomplished only when the electron absorbed energy from somewhere else. Jumping to a lower rung, though, the electron would have to give off energy. The amount of energy absorbed or given off was not just any old random amount, either. It was one quantum, or packet, of energy.

The size of the quantum differed for every wavelength of energy, Planck said. But, in all cases, it was equal to the frequency of the wave multiplied by a certain quantity that was always the same. Planck gave this quantity the symbol h, but today it is known as "Planck's constant." Numerically, it works out to 66 ten-thousandths of a trillionth of a trillionth.

The shorter a wave, of course, the higher the frequency. Since Planck's constant remains the same in every instance, the size of the quantum increases as the wavelength gets shorter. Red light, which has a long wavelength and thus a low frequency, has relatively small quanta. Orange light has larger quanta, yellow light still larger quanta, violet light even larger quanta. Beyond the visible spectrum, such high-frequency radiations as X rays and gamma rays have very large quanta indeed.

Max Planck saw the quantum as a kind of particle. This revived Isaac Newton's old theory that light consisted of separate particles, a concept which had long since given way to the theory that light was a wave. But Planck never thought of the quantum as a particle of the same sort as electrons and protons and neutrons. Those particles (which, of course, were discovered years after Planck first stated his theory) are the same in all matter, whereas quanta can be quite different in size, depending on the frequency of the radiation they comprise.

Planck was uneasy about his theory, and did all he could to avoid a complete break with classical physics. The man who pushed quantum theory into totally new ground was a younger German, Albert Einstein (1879–1955)—probably the best-known physicist of our time.

Einstein, born in the town of Ulm in Bavaria, studied mathematics and physics at the Polytechnic School in Switzerland from 1896 to 1900—the exciting years when Roentgen, Becquerel, Thomson, Planck, and the Curies were announcing their bewildering new ideas. Einstein became a Swiss citizen and, in 1902, took a job as examiner of patents in the Swiss Patent Office at Berne. The job paid enough to support Einstein, his wife, and a growing family, which was more than physics would do. Despite his obvious brilliance, Einstein had found himself unable to find a teaching job in any university in 1902. So by day he worked in a government office and by night he feverishly covered pads of paper with the equations that soon would startle the world of science.

One of the many fields of inquiry that attracted Einstein was the problem of the photoelectric effect. This was the effect produced when a beam of light, and particularly a beam of ultraviolet rays or X rays, fell upon a surface of metal, knocking electrons loose. The stronger the beam, the more electrons were knocked loose. But the speed with which the electrons flew away from the metal depended, not on the strength of the beam, but on its wavelength. Violet light could impart a greater jolt to the electrons than red light, and X rays gave an even bigger "kick" to the electrons.

Einstein applied Planck's thinking to the problem. Each electron was knocked loose, he said, as a result of a collision between a single "energy element" of light and an atom. (Einstein coined the word *quantum* at this point to replace Planck's longer term, "energy element." Today, quanta are usually called *photons*, from the Greek word *photos*, "light.")

The energy with which the electrons were jarred loose, Einstein said, could be related to the energy of the quanta striking the metal. He used Planck's constant—h times the frequency of the light, represented by the Greek letter v (pronounced "nu"). The energy of the fleeing electrons was equal to hv, minus W, representing the energy spent by the electron in the struggle to escape from the metal atom.

Einstein thus had showed that light acted as though made up of particles. He did not come right out and say that light actually *did* consist of particles. He simply put it that the photoelectric effect was best explained by assuming that light acted *as though* it were made up of particles. Einstein was not ready to junk the wave theory of light entirely, because other experiments, such as Fresnel's in the early part of the nineteenth century, had strongly indicated that light was a wave.

Einstein and Planck had demonstrated that atoms emitted and absorbed light only in certain definite units, the quanta or photons. Now, in 1913, the great Danish physicist Niels Bohr applied quantum theory to the atom itself—with stunning results.

You will remember that, in 1911, Rutherford had proposed a model of the atom in which the electrons circled the nucleus like planets around a sun. But Rutherford himself had written, "The analogy, however, must not be pressed too far." Under the classical theory, the rotating electrons had to give off energy constantly. Eventually, they would lose all their energy and collapse into the nucleus. But no fire burns forever. Sooner or later there is no energy left, and the fire burns down. How could electrons radiate energy forever? Either Rutherford's model of the atom had to be thrown out, or else the laws of physics as they were then known.

Bohr scrapped the laws of physics. It was a bold stroke on the part of a man of twenty-eight. Having studied briefly with Rutherford at Manchester in 1912, Bohr returned to Denmark, and, in March, 1913, wrote to Rutherford explaining his new ideas.

The accepted laws of physics, Bohr argued, simply did not apply in the almost infinitely small world of the atom. The atom obeyed laws of its own, which happened to be the special laws of quantum physics.

Bohr accepted Rutherford's idea of electrons revolving around a central nucleus. But, he said, the electrons could revolve only in certain orbits whose distances from the nucleus could be computed mathematically. So long as the atom remained undisturbed, the electrons would remain in their orbits indefinitely, according to Bohr, radiating no energy. Even though the electron is negative and the nucleus is positive, an electron would stay in what Bohr called a "stationary state," unaffected by the electrical forces which classical physics said would necessarily draw it inward. "For each atom," Bohr wrote, "there exists a number of definite states of motion called stationary states, in which the atom can exist without radiating energy."

When an atom was disturbed—by some outside force such as X rays, alpha particles, or even heat—the electrons began to jump from orbit to orbit. These jumps did not occur at random. When an electron jumped, it moved to another permitted orbit. An electron absorbing a quantum of energy would jump from a smaller to a larger permitted orbit. When an electron dropped back from an outer orbit to an inner one, it emitted a quantum of energy. The atoms of each element gave off energy at wavelengths unique to the element, which was how the spectroscope could identify different elements.

Bohr worked out his model of the atom at first only with hydrogen, which has the simplest atom of all—just one electron and one proton. He computed the possible orbits for that single electron. Under normal conditions, the electron would tend to remain in the orbit closest to the nucleus. But when the electron absorbed energy from the outside it entered an "excited state" and jumped outward, one orbit for each quantum absorbed, until it reached the outermost permitted orbit. As the electron tumbled back from orbit to orbit it emitted quanta of light, at the particular frequencies of hydrogen's familiar lines in the spectrum.

Working out a model for hydrogen's atom was relatively simple. More complicated atoms posed tougher problems. How were the 28 electrons of nickel arranged in their orbits? How were silver's 47 electrons arranged? Uranium's 92?

Long before Bohr's quantum-theory approach, J. J. Thomson had suggested that the electrons were arranged in rings with specific numbers of electrons in each ring—5 in the first ring, 16 in the second, and so on. Bohr's work showed that this plan would not do, but the basic idea of concentric rings still had merit. An American, Gilbert N. Lewis of the University of California, put forth in 1916 an atomic model in which the electrons were arranged in imaginary fixed zones, or "shells," around the nucleus. Three years later, Irving Langmuir of the General Electric Co. improved this idea so that it could be used to explain chemical activity.

Langmuir started with two elements that had no chemical

activity at all—helium, atomic number 2, and neon, atomic number 10. These two elements refused to enter into chemical combinations with any other elements.

Langmuir argued that the helium and neon atoms must be so stable that they were incapable of chemical activity. Helium, then, must have only one shell of electrons, containing two electrons. All elements have a tendency to complete the outermost shell of electrons by chemical combination. Since helium did not combine, its single shell must be complete with two electrons.

An atom with more than two electrons would then need a second shell. So lithium, with three electrons, would have a complete inner shell of two, and then a single electron in the outer shell. Beryllium, the next element, would have two electrons in the outer shell; boron, three electrons; carbon, four; and so on. But then comes neon, the tenth element, which again does not combine. So its second shell, Langmuir reasoned, must be complete with eight electrons. Heavier elements need a third shell.

The next noncombining element is argon, 8 elements along. Then comes krypton, 18 places up the table, and xenon, 18 places beyond, and finally radon, another 18 places on. Extending his reasoning, Langmuir showed that electrons were probably arranged with shells that contained—from the inside outward—a maximum of 2, 8, 8, 18, 18, and 18 electrons. The heaviest elements, those beyond radon, had 6 complete shells of electrons, plus an incomplete seventh shell.

The incomplete outer shell, furthermore, was where all chemical activity took place. Langmuir suggested that atoms tended either to lose or gain electrons in the outer shell, depending on whether that shell contained few or many. Chlorine, element number 17, has its 17 electrons arranged this way: 2 in the innermost shell, 8 in the next shell, and 7 in the outermost. So chlorine atoms are constantly in quest of the eighth electron that would fill its outer ring. Chlorine is thus an "electron-taker." Sodium, on the other hand, has 11 electrons—2 in the innermost shell, 8 in the second shell, and only one in the outermost. So sodium is a good "electron-loser." What more natural thing is there, chemically speaking, than for an atom of sodium and one of chlorine to come together? Sodium loses its extra electron to chlorine, and the result is a chemical compound, sodium chloride—table salt.

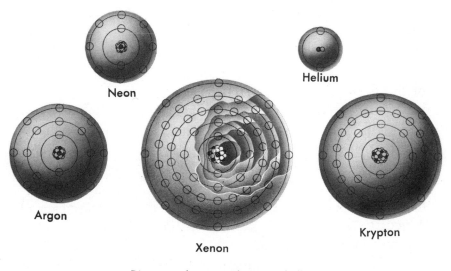

Diagram showing Electron Shells

Oxygen, similarly, has 8 electrons—2 in the inner shell, 6 in the outer shell. It "needs" two more electrons. Along comes hydrogen, with one lonesome electron in its single shell.

Each oxygen atom attracts two hydrogen atoms, giving us the water molecule—whose chemical symbol, of course, is H_2O.

Something that had been quite mysterious since 1869 made sense now. Remember Mendeleev and his table of the elements. He had discovered a pattern of relationships which repeated themselves every 8 elements at the lighter end of the list, every 18 elements further on. It was not just a coincidence, it could be seen now. The strange relationships between the elements depended on the number of electrons in their outer rings. Fluorine, chlorine, bromine, and iodine hold positions 9, 17, 35, and 53 in the table. Their places are thus 8, 18, and 18 elements apart. Following Langmuir's arrangement, it can be seen that all four of these closely related, chemically similar elements must have one electron missing in the outer shell.

Other chemical "families" in the list of elements followed the same 8, 8, 18, 18 spacing. Langmuir had solved the riddle of the periodic table. He showed that it was the electrons of an atom—not the nucleus—that took part in chemical reactions. And he supplied a sound and logical reason for the relationships Mendeleev had discovered.

Of course, Langmuir had never seen the shells of an atom. He had never actually counted the electrons in any shell. He had simply proposed a theory. But the theory cleared up old difficulties without raising any new difficulties of its own, and it is still basically accepted today.

However, Langmuir's model of the atom is a chemist's model. It is designed to answer only the questions of chemistry, the science of how elements combine. So far as physicists were concerned, Langmuir's model was an oversimplification. It pictured the electrons and the nucleus practically as tiny solid particles. That was good enough to explain chemical compounds—but the physicists wanted to build on Bohr's revolutionary theory of 1913 and find out what the atom and its components *really* looked like.

The new research reached its first great peak in the years just after World War I. A group of brilliant young physicists poured forth a torrent of unusual ideas which are still difficult for laymen to understand. Before long, they had established a strange and baffling new picture of atomic events.

First came experimental confirmation of the quantum theory itself. In 1911, Robert A. Millikan of the University of Chicago had performed a classical experiment, called the "oil-drop" experiment, in which he was able to isolate a single electron, determine its electrical charge, and even weigh it relative to an atom of hydrogen. Five years later, Millikan performed another experiment in which he used the photo-electric effect to determine the exact value of Planck's constant. Millikan's figure, arrived at in the laboratory, agreed closely with Planck's own figure, derived by purely mathematical means. For these two accomplishments, Millikan received the 1923 Nobel Prize in Physics. (Millikan, who lived from 1868 to 1953, is one of the great names in American physics. But, like that other great man of physics, Einstein, Millikan never took himself too seriously. Once, at a dinner given in honor of both Einstein and Millikan, the two great men were seen feverishly scribbling on a sheet of paper, passing it back from one to the other. An onlooker wondered what stunning new theory of the universe was being born at the dinner table—only to find out that Einstein and Millikan were simply playing tic-tac-toe!)

Another important experiment, also rewarded by a Nobel prize, was Arthur Holly Compton's discovery of the "Compton effect." He showed that, when a beam of X rays was bounced off a block of carbon, the reflected beam had a longer wavelength, and thus a lower frequency, than the original beam. The wave theory of light would not account for such a loss of energy. But it could easily be explained in terms of quantum theory, by saying that the photons making up the X-ray beam lost energy when they collided with the electrons of the carbon.

Compton—and Einstein before him—had provided proof that light was apparently composed of particles. Yet other experiments only made sense when light was thought of as a wave.

Particle or wave? Wave or particle?

The embarrassing conclusion that the physicists drew was that light behaves as a wave at some times, and as a stream of particles at others. The problem is that words are not really adequate to describe the events of the atomic world. Such words as "wave" and "particle" are only rough and inexact descriptions of the world of the infinitely small. Electro-magnetic radiation could not be pinned down so easily into one category or the other. We can look at a stack of apples, and say, "particles." We can look at the ripples in a pond, and say, "waves." But drawing the line is more difficult when we are dealing with light or gamma rays or some other form of electromagnetic radiation.

In 1924, Louis de Broglie (1892–   ), a French physicist and a member of a noble family of old Europe, showed mathe-matically that the motion of electrons was guided by "waves," which Prince de Broglie called "pilot waves." (They are sometimes called "de Broglie waves" today.) A very simple parallel would compare the electron and its pilot wave to a boat surrounded by ripples. But, of course, electrons are not really boats, nor is a de Broglie wave a ripple.

The new idea supported Bohr's model of the atom. De

Broglie showed that the possible electron orbits were limited by the wavelengths of the pilot waves. Bohr had calculated that the distances of the successive electrons from the nucleus had to be in the ratio of whole numbers squared—1, 4, 9, 16, 25, and so on. But he did not know why. De Broglie's calculation showed that his theoretical pilot waves would fit into Bohr's scheme of orbits, if the length of each wave equaled Planck's constant divided by the mass and the velocity of the electron in that orbit.

In 1927, two American engineers, C. J. Davisson and L. H. Germer of the Bell Telephone Laboratories, carried out experiments with a beam of electrons that proved the existence of de Broglie's pilot waves. They found electron "wavelengths" that agreed exactly with de Broglie's calculations.

This wave within the atom should not be confused with electromagnetic radiation. The pilot waves are something else entirely—not part of the electromagnetic spectrum, but of the atomic structure.

De Broglie had shown mathematically, and Davisson and Germer experimentally, that electrons, as well as light, had some wave characteristics and some particle characteristics. Other physicists of the same general group—Erwin Schrödinger, P. A. M. Dirac, and Max Born—put forth their own equations explaining the nature of atoms, electrons, and light. To follow their work, it was necessary to accept the fact that they were talking about waves possessing properties of particles, and particles possessing properties of waves. Total confusion faced physics. Electrons and photons, it seemed, were both waves and particles all at once—but what did that mean?

The German physicist Werner Heisenberg brought science out of its bewilderment in 1927 with his "principle of uncertainty." Heisenberg, who had been in the vanguard of the little group of men that remade the theory of physics early in the 1920's, said that it was futile to try to peer too deeply into the ultimate structure of things. It was impossible ever to make really accurate observations of atomic events. Not merely was it practically impossible; it was *fundamentally* impossible.

Heisenberg put it this way:

"From experiments it is seen that . . . matter and radiation . . . sometimes exhibit the properties of waves, at other times those of particles. Now it it obvious that a thing cannot be a form of wave motion and composed of particles at the same time—the two concepts are too different.

"It is not surprising that our language should be incapable of describing the processes occurring within the atoms, for, as has been remarked, it was invented to describe the experiences of daily life, and these consist only of processes involving exceedingly large numbers of atoms. Furthermore . . . words can only describe things of which we can form mental pictures."

Quantum theory, he said, had given some insight into the atomic world. But that insight was limited by a fatal flaw. To make observations of electrons, we must use photons—since no observations can be carried out without light. But on the atomic level the photons themselves would disturb the state of the electrons and make the observations meaningless. As Heisenberg put it, "Every experiment destroys some of the knowledge of the system which was obtained by previous experiments."

To understand the nature of the electron fully, it would be necessary to know its motion. We can study the motion of a ping-pong ball without having to allow for the impact of photons on the ball as it moves. The ball is so big compared to photons that they cannot deflect it in any significant way. But suppose we were able to isolate a single electron, and tried to measure its velocity and its exact position. To do so we would have to let light strike it, and there, Heisenberg said, was the rub.

If we used high-frequency light, the energetic photons would knock the electron off its course, changing its velocity at the very moment we tried to measure it. Using lower-frequency light, the electron would be disturbed very little. But such light of long wavelengths would give a hazy image, so we would have only a vague idea of the electron's exact position.

We cannot have it both ways. We can measure an electron's position, or we can measure an electron's velocity. But since the very act of measuring one or the other fatally disturbs or obscures the experiment, we cannot measure both position and velocity at the same time. Thus we can never attain exact knowledge of a particle in the atomic world.

The best we can do, Heisenberg said, is measure *probabilities*. Atomic events are uncertain. We cannot pin down an electron to any one position; rather, the best we can do is calculate the probable position of an electron along a given orbit. Instead of thinking of electrons as individual particles, we must think of them as blurs, and so they have something of the nature of both waves and particles.

It is dangerous to try to simplify such difficult thinking by using examples drawn from the ordinary world. But consider a baseball. Certainly it is a hard, individual object—a "particle." What do we see when a batter hits a hard line drive? We see just a white blur as the ball travels away from home plate at a terrific speed. Our eyes are not good enough to detect the baseball itself at such a speed. All we see is the path of the ball—a "wave."

So it might seem that a baseball could be a particle at some times and a wave at other times. However, if we took a series of fast-action photographs of the path of the ball, we would see the ball as a "particle" again, speeding along its path. What Heisenberg says is that it is impossible, on the atomic level, to take such pictures. The very act of taking them knocks the "ball"—the electron—out of its path and renders our observation useless. So, while we have ways of explaining the wave-and-particle nature of a moving baseball, we have no way of accounting for the apparent wave-and-particle nature of an electron.

Not every physicist accepted Heisenberg's uncertainty principle. One who never liked it was Albert Einstein. To the end of his life, Einstein fought against the idea that ultimate knowledge of the atom might be withheld from us. But even Einstein failed to offer any real attack against the idea of un-certainty. The one time that he thought he had found the flaw in Heisenberg's thinking, Niels Bohr showed that it was Einstein who had erred.

The mathematical thinking of Heisenberg, de Broglie, Bohr, Born, Schrödinger, and others of the 1920's made the nature of the atom a difficult thing for the layman to grasp. But it is not necessary to follow the new thinkers all the way to understand the basic picture that emerged.

The Bohr model of the atom, as modified in the 1920's by new ideas, consisted of a positive nucleus around which elec-trons moved. The electrons were grouped in orbits whose spac-ing was determined according to the wave mathematics of de Broglie. When an electron absorbed energy from outside the atom, it leaped up to an outer orbit. Falling back to its own orbit, it gave off energy—as electromagnetic radiation—and the wavelength depended on the amount of energy given off.

An important feature of this theory was supplied in 1925 by the Austrian-born Wolfgang Pauli (1900–1958). Pauli's "exclusion principle" showed that no more than two electrons could occupy the same quantum orbit. When these vacancies are filled, the next orbit must be occupied.

This should not be confused with Langmuir's picture of electron shells. The Bohr-Pauli picture uses a group of orbits within each shell. The first shell, as we have seen, can contain no more than two electrons. Normally—according to Pauli—these two would be in the same orbit. But there are several possible orbits within the shell to which the electrons could jump in an "excited state." Atoms more complicated than those of hydrogen or helium have a second shell, which can hold up to eight electrons—and, again following Pauli, those eight electrons must be distributed on four orbits within that shell.

Many years after Pauli first suggested this, it was found that electrons not only had an electrical charge, but also were tiny magnets. They were found to spin rapidly as they orbit around the nucleus, and this spinning sets up magnetic forces. Electrons can spin in one of two ways: either in the direction in which they travel along their orbits, or the other way. Physicists showed that the two electrons traveling in the same orbit must spin in opposite directions from each other. This sets up weak magnetic fields, disturbing the orbits slightly. So the Pauli exclusion principle had to be revised. It is now thought that two electrons thought to be traveling in the same orbit really occupy two different but very similar orbits.

We are very far, now, from the fairly simple concept of the atom of the years before World War I. For their work in penetrating the atomic mysteries, Bohr, Planck, de Broglie, Schrödinger, Dirac, Heisenberg, Langmuir, Born, and Pauli all eventually received Nobel prizes, the highest formal recognition of a scientist's work. They opened new horizons of thinking. They made the world of physics a very different sort of place.

7

SMASHING THE ATOM

M OST OF THE WORK described in the last chapter was done on paper. It was theory work, brilliant and abstruse. Atomic physics advances on two fronts at once, though. While some scientists work out equations, others perform laboratory experiments. And, while one group of physicists was pondering waves and particles, others were trying to smash atoms apart to discover their basic nature.

As far back as 1919, Rutherford had been smashing and changing the atoms of light elements. We have seen how he bombarded nitrogen with alpha particles, producing hydrogen ions (protons) and oxygen atoms. In the years that followed, Rutherford and his fellow workers knocked protons out of the nuclei of most of the lighter atoms. And Blackett, in 1925, showed that the alpha particle "bullets" actually entered the nuclei of the bombarded atoms, thus changing their atomic numbers and atomic weights.

There was good reason to want to continue such experiments. Not only would theoretical knowledge about the atom be gained—but there was the possibility (remote, but real) that some day man might find a way of harnessing the energy of the atom.

What was that atomic energy? Where did it come from?

Once again we have to backtrack—to 1905, to that Swiss patent official named Einstein. 1905 was the year Einstein did his work on the photoelectric effect, but that was only a small part of his achievement that year. His most revolutionary accomplishment of 1905 was his special theory of relativity, which answered many troublesome questions about the nature of space and time. Only one part of that theory concerns us directly: Einstein's concept of the relationship between matter and energy.

Physicists define "energy" as the capacity for doing work. Work, in the term of physics, is the application of a force— the performance of some exertion that puts a body in motion. When a weight of a pound is lifted one foot, physicists say that "one foot-pound of work" has been done.

A coiled spring contains energy, because it can uncoil and lash back to its original shape, and that is a kind of work. Physicists call the energy of a coiled spring *potential* energy, because it is not yet in action. An office safe dangling from a rope high above the street has potential energy. If that safe should break loose and fall, the people it landed on would experience its *kinetic* energy—the energy of a body in motion.

As part of his theory of relativity, Einstein showed that the faster a body moves, the greater its mass becomes. The mass of an electron traveling at close to the speed of light, Einstein said, is greater than the mass of an electron at rest. Einstein worked out this famous equation to indicate the relationship between mass and energy:

$$E = mc^2$$

Since that is the equation that governs the explosion of an atomic bomb, it is probably the most important and the most terrifying equation ever written. But what does it mean?

Einstein held that any change in the energy of a body is accompanied by a change in its mass. The equation shows mathematically how these changes are related. E stands for energy, m for mass, and c for the speed of light through a vacuum, a factor that never changes.

Matter and energy, Einstein showed, are really forms of the same thing. This fits in with two laws already known—the law of the conservation of matter, and the law of the conservation of energy. The first of those laws shows that matter can be changed from one form to another—in evaporating, water changes from a liquid to a gas—but that matter can never be destroyed or created. The second law makes it clear that energy also can be changed from one form to another, but neither created nor destroyed. When we coil a spring, we are putting potential energy into it through our work. When that spring snaps back, it gives off the same amount of energy. No new energy has been created, and none has been lost.

Einstein demonstrated that when matter is apparently "destroyed," a certain amount of energy is created. When energy is "destroyed," matter is created. When matter is converted into energy, Einstein proved, the amount of energy formed (E) equals the amount of matter involved (m), multiplied by the speed of light (c) squared.

Substituting real figures for Einstein's algebraic symbols gives some startling results. Mass is measured in grams (453.6 grams to the pound). The speed of light is about 186,000 miles a second, but it is often expressed in centimeters (2.54 centimeters to the inch). In centimeters, the speed of light is 30 billion centimeters per second—which must be multiplied by itself to get Einstein's c^2. Working it all out, we would find that for 1 pound of matter, E = 400,000,000,000,000,000,-000,000 ergs of energy, ergs being the usual unit of measuring energy. Translating that into more familiar terms, we discover that if a pound of matter could be completely transformed into energy, it would release as much energy as the explosion of 10 million tons of TNT. Put another way, a pound of matter would release energy equal to all the electricity produced in the United States in an average month.

Of course, when Einstein worked all this out, he never imagined that men would learn to release such gigantic forces. The only ways we had of obtaining energy were extremely inefficient. That was why we needed 10 million tons of TNT to release the same amount of energy that could be obtained, under perfect conditions, from a single pound of matter.

Matter was just "bottled energy," in Einstein's equation. And, since matter was made up of atoms, each atom itself contained energy. As early as 1903, Rutherford and Soddy, investigating the energies of alpha particles, had written, "The energy latent in the atom must be enormous." Albert Einstein, in 1905, had given an exact figure for the potential energy involved. Then, in 1919, Rutherford's pioneering atom-smashing experiments actually succeeded in changing energy into mass.

He bombarded nitrogen nuclei with helium nuclei, producing oxygen and a proton. An exact computation showed a total atomic weight for the nitrogen and alpha particle of 18.01140. The total atomic weight of the end product of the collision, the oxygen and proton, was 18.01268. Mass of 0.00128 had been gained in the experiment. But not created out of nothingness. It had come from the kinetic energy of the alpha particle. Einstein's equation held true.

What about getting energy out of a reaction, by giving up mass?

That could be done too. A little calculating shows that when protons and neutrons are welded together to form atoms, a certain amount of mass is "lost" in the welding process. For example, the helium nucleus has an atomic weight of 4.00280. It consists of two neutrons and two protons. If we were to add up to the weights of those four particles individually, we would get a figure 0.0303 heavier than a helium nucleus. So the joining of the four particles somehow uses up that much mass. Where does it go? It is converted into potential energy, the so-called "binding energy" of the nucleus. To knock that nucleus apart, we would have to give it a jolt of an energy greater than that.

The energy of the atomic world is measured in terms of *electron volts*. A volt is the unit of measure of electrical force. An electron volt is the amount of energy acquired by an electron given a "kick" of 1 volt. The binding energy of a helium nucleus is 28.2 million electron volts, abbreviated 28.2 Mev.

The more complex an atom, the greater the binding energy that holds it together. Uranium has a binding energy of 1.8 *billion* electron volts, or 1.8 Bev. If a uranium atom could be broken into its more than 200 neutrons and protons, that much energy would be given off. Even partly breaking up the uranium nucleus would release a great deal of energy.

Atomic scientists sought for some way to break up the nucleus. The radioactive elements, which tended to break apart of their own accord, supplied an artillery of atomic "bullets" that could be used to smash more stable nuclei apart: alpha particles. Rutherford used alpha particles in his pioneering atom-smashing experiments.

But alpha particles have certain disadvantages. They carry

a double positive charge. The nucleus, too, has a positive charge. So the nucleus and the alpha particle tend to repel each other. A stream of alpha particles scores few direct hits when aimed at atomic nuclei. Some other particle, without such a strong positive charge, might be better ammunition.

In the 1920's, only two other particles could possibly be used: electrons and protons. Electrons, with their negative charges would not be electrically repelled by nuclei. But they were regarded as too light to serve as atom smashers. Protons, though positively charged, have only half the charge of an alpha particle, so they might serve. Unfortunately, the proton is only a quarter as heavy as an alpha particle. Using protons instead of alpha particles would be like using a 4-pound bowling ball instead of a 16-pound ball.

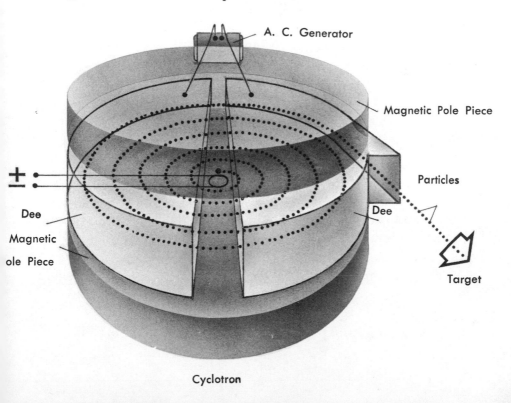

Cyclotron

But even a very light ball can knock down the pins if it is only thrown hard enough. Scientists looked for some way to speed up protons to make them good atom smashers.

Getting a supply of protons was no great task. Sending an electric charge through hydrogen would ionize the hydrogen atom, leaving just the nucleus—which, in hydrogen, is simply a proton. In 1929, two men of Rutherford's Cambridge laboratory, J. D. Cockcroft and E. T. S. Walton, built a device called a voltage multiplier, which could be used to produce high-speed protons.

The voltage multiplier consists of a long glass tube pumped free of air. At the top of the tube is a proton source. In the tube are a series of metal cylinders. Each cylinder carries an electric charge. As the protons enter the tube, they are drawn into the first metal cylinder, and pick up speed. They are hurled downward from cylinder to cylinder, and each time their speed increases until they come out traveling much faster than when they went in.

Cockcroft and Walton began with the element lithium, atomic number 3. Bombarding its nucleus with high-speed protons, they were able to split it in two. The proton bullet joined with one of the protons and two of the neutrons of the lithium nucleus. The other two protons and the remaining two neutrons clung together. The result was two alpha particles, each with two protons and two neutrons! The total mass of the two alpha particles was 0.0186 atomic mass units (amu) less than the combined mass of the proton and lithium nucleus at the start of the experiment. The missing mass, equal to 17.32 Mev, was carried off in the form of energy. So Cockcroft and Walton had liberated some of the energy of the atom!

But no power plants could operate on that sort of energy.

The trouble was that the scientists used up more energy accelerating their protons than they could get from smashing the nucleus. Only a few protons out of a million caused the energy-liberating reaction. The rest bounced harmlessly away. So the process was highly inefficient. But still, it was a beginning.

Other researchers were developing different kinds of atom smashers. In America, Robert van de Graaf built a high-voltage generator that developed an electric charge by carrying a silk conveyor belt past a comb of sharp needles from an electric generator. Another American, Ernest Orlando Lawrence, was even more successful in his attempt to design a particle accelerator.

Lawrence (1901–1958) was born in South Dakota. His grandparents on both sides were Norwegians who had come to America as pioneer settlers in the middle of the nineteenth century. When he was a boy, he became fascinated by the new field of radio communication, then for a while gave his allegiance to medicine. But physics claimed him, finally. He went to the University of South Dakota, did graduate work at the University of Minnesota and at Yale, and finally, in 1928, joined the physics faculty of the University of California.

In the spring of 1929 Lawrence began work on a machine to impart a high velocity to particles. The method he had in mind has been compared, by one scientist, to "a child in a swing. By properly synchronizing the pushes, the child may be made to swing very high even though each individual push would lift him only a short distance."

Lawrence, a man of boundless energy and innumerable ideas, had his first model ready by January, 1930. Basically it consisted of a magnet and a metal box. The box was placed between the poles of the magnet. It contained two semicircular

Ernest O. Lawrence

electrodes, which Lawrence called "dees," because they were D-shaped. The dees were connected to a high-frequency electric current.

An ion source admitted protons to the box. The protons moved toward the gap between the dees. One dee had a positive charge, the other a negative charge, and an electric field existed in the gap. The proton, with its positive charge, was attracted toward the negative dee. As it passed across the gap, this attraction increased its speed as if by a sudden jerk.

The proton then swung in a semicircle around the dee. When it approached the gap again, the voltage in the electrodes was suddenly reversed, so that now the other dee had the negative charge. Again the proton was jerked across the gap—gaining even more speed. Round and round the proton sped, picking up speed each time it crossed the gap. However, centrifugal force also drove the proton outward from the center of the box, until finally it reached the rim and could be fired outward as a high-speed atomic bullet.

Lawrence called his machine a cyclotron, because it whirled the protons in circles. His first model was only a few inches in diameter. Soon he built a slightly more ambitious one that could give protons an energy of 80,000 electron volts, using a force of only 2,000 volts to do it. By February, 1932, Lawrence had built a cyclotron 11 inches across, which could kick protons up to energies of 1,200,000 electron volts.

Lawrence was only beginning. He had dreams of building really huge cyclotrons. The bigger the cyclotron, though, the more powerful a magnet he needed to create a field in which the charged particles could circle. Luck was with him. In 1918, the Federal Telegraph Co. had built a big magnet, weighing 60 tons, for use in a radio transmitter intended for China. The station had never been built, and the magnet was lying useless in storage in California. Lawrence found out about it, and wangled the monstrous magnet for his cyclotron. With it, he built an 85-ton cyclotron that contained 8 tons of copper wire alone. As atomic research progressed, even that became obsolete. Lawrence's next cyclotron, built in 1939, weighed 225 tons and could boost hydrogen ions to an energy of 60,000,000 electron volts, or 60 Mev.

The 1939 cyclotron seems like a toy today. After World War II, another Lawrence cyclotron was constructed at California capable of yielding energy ranges of 400 Mev. It is somewhat different in principle from earlier cyclotrons, and is called a synchrocyclotron. Another postwar kind of atom smasher is the betatron, which accelerates electrons to great velocities. As the electrons approach the speed of light, they increase as much as 200 times in mass, according to Einstein's relativity theory. Thus they become more useful as atomic "ammunition." Another electron accelerator is the synchrotron, which has attained energies of more than 300 Mev.

Then there are the most powerful accelerators of all, the proton synchrotrons, which are enormous in size and operate in the *billion*-electron-volt range. It is almost futile to write about these monsters, because seemingly a newer and more powerful one is constructed somewhere every few months. The first proton synchrotron, at the Brookhaven National Laboratory on Long Island, reached energies of 3 Bev. In March, 1954, a proton sychrotron called the bevatron went into operation at the University of California, reaching up into the 6-Bev range. Then the Soviet Union built a 10-Bev accelerator, and Brookhaven surpassed it with a proton synchrotron heading toward the 35-Bev range. The race to build bigger particle accelerators does not seem to be over yet, judging from plans now afoot, even though the newest accelerators cost hundreds of millions of dollars and are many times bigger than a football field.

We are far ahead of our story now. Let's return to the early 1930's, when the first puny particle accelerators were being built.

In 1930, we noted a few chapters ago, two German experimenters named Bothe and Becker bombarded beryllium with alpha particles and found that a strangely penetrating ray was given off. Two years later, James Chadwick identified that ray as being a stream of neutrons, the electrically uncharged, proton-sized particles of the atomic nucleus.

Two other scientists were attracted by the Bothe–Becker findings. They were the French physicists Frédéric Joliot and his wife Irène. As is often done in Europe, Joliot had joined his wife's maiden name to his own, so that they became Mr. and Mrs. Joliot-Curie. For Mrs. Irène Joliot was none other than the eldest daughter of the famed Marie Curie. Born in 1897, Irène had been barely old enough to understand what was happening when her parents received the Nobel prize. She was six years old then. Young Irène had many opportunities to watch her brilliant parents at work. The Curies gave Irène and her younger sister Eve private instruction in science. Eve's gifts were chiefly literary, it later turned out, but Irène had inherited her parents' love of science.

When she was nine, Irène Curie tragically lost her father. Five years later, she and her mother journeyed to Stockholm when Madame Curie received her second Nobel prize. During World War I, the teenage Irène worked in the X-ray laboratories her mother had helped to establish, and after the war began studies of her own into the mysteries of radioactivity.

About the same time, she met Frédéric Joliot, three years her junior. He had studied engineering, physics, and chemistry at the School of Physics and Chemistry in Paris, where the elder Curies had done their first radium experiments. He took his degree in 1923, and soon took a job in Madame Curie's laboratory, the Institute of Radium. A friendship quickly grew between the young assistant and Madame Curie's daughter Irène. In 1926, Irène Curie duplicated her mother's scientific love story by marrying her fellow worker.

It was a collaboration that would last for almost 30 years.

The Joliot-Curies became the leading atomic scientists of France, as well as working actively in the world peace movement. In 1935 they received the Nobel Chemistry Prize for their work with artificial radioactivity. Their partnership was broken only by Irène's death, in 1956. The disease that killed her was the same that had taken the life of her famous mother: leukemia, caused by overexposure to atomic radiation during long years in the laboratory. He husband died two years later.

Madame Curie was in the last year of her life when, in 1933, the Joliot-Curies made atomic history. They repeated the Bothe-Becker experiments with beryllium, and just missed discovering the neutron. Experimenting with other elements, though, they bombarded aluminum with alpha particles and achieved an unusual result.

Aluminum has 13 protons and 14 neutrons in its nucleus, for an atomic weight of 27. When the Joliot-Curies sent an alpha particle crashing into the aluminum nucleus, they added 2 protons, raising the nucleus to an atomic number of 15. The element with that atomic number is phosphorus. So they had artifically transmuted aluminum into phosphorus. This, though, was not at all different from Rutherford's work with nitrogen almost 15 years before.

In the reaction, a neutron was given off. That left 15 neutrons in the nucleus, and so the phosphorus created had an atomic weight of 30. Normal phosphorus has an atomic weight of 31. Thus the Joliot-Curies had created a new isotope of phosphorus. The artificial creation of isotopes was not new either.

What *was* new was this: the laboratory-made phosphorus was radioactive!

Until that time, the only radioactive elements known were the extremely heavy ones, those with an atomic number greater than lead (82). All the elements heavier than lead were radioactive. But no naturally occurring radioactive elements lighter than lead were known. (Today we know about 15 natural radioactive isotopes of the lighter elements, such as carbon-14 and potassium-40.)

The phosphorus-30 created by the Joliot-Curies was radioactively unstable. Its nucleus tended to give off particles spontaneously, just as radium and uranium atoms did. But the particle that phosphorus-30 gave off was most novel. It had the positive charge of a proton, but the tiny mass of an electron. A positive electron!

Such a particle did not come as a surprise. In 1930, the theoretical physicist P. A. M. Dirac had worked out certain equations that showed both a positive and a negative value for the electron. The equations were immediately challenged, but Dirac stuck to his guns. And within two years the existence of the positively charged electron was no longer in doubt.

In 1932, at the Kellogg Radiation Laboratory of the California Institute of Technology, twenty-seven-year-old Carl D. Anderson was working with the great Robert Millikan on the study of cosmic rays, a high-energy form of radiation that bombards the earth from space. Anderson took thousands of cloud-chamber photographs of cosmic rays as they struck atoms of gas.

On August 2, 1932, Anderson developed a photograph that made little sense at first look. A cosmic ray had broken an atom apart, and one of the tracks left by the atom's fragments was like that of an electron—except that it went in the wrong direction. It could not be a proton, for its fog track was ten times as long as a proton's would have been. Anderson finally concluded that it was a positively charged particle with the mass of an electron. He named it the *positron*.

Later work has shown that the positron can be formed when a gamma ray, an X ray, or some other form of high-frequency radiation strikes matter. The ray splits into a positron–electron pair. Thus energy (the ray) becomes matter (the two particles). Why two particles? Because there seems to be a law of conservation of electric charge in the universe. When a particle with charge is created out of energy, it must be accompanied by an identical particle of opposite charge. Thus the positive positron and the negative electron cancel each other out, and no new electric charge has really been created.

The cancelling is done not only mathematically but actually. A positron's lifespan is extremely short. In less than a billionth of a second, it attracts the nearest electron and the two particles annihilate each other. When this happens, a gamma ray is formed. So the process works in both directions. Energy may become matter, and the matter becomes energy again. When a positron and an electron collide and destroy each other, the energy of the gamma ray that is produced exactly fits Einstein's equation, $E = mc^2$.

The importance of Anderson's discovery was recognized by the Nobel prize committee in 1936. As soon as his work was announced, late in 1932, other scientists began looking for positrons, and the Joliot-Curies found them. Positrons were given off during the bombardment of aluminum. But the positrons continued to appear after the alpha-particle bombardment was stopped. As one well-known scientist put it, "If you stop using a nutcracker, you expect the nuts to stop cracking."

The newly formed phosphorus-30 atoms were unstable. They quickly disintegrated by giving off a positron. The effect of this was to subtract one positive charge from the atomic nucleus. One of the protons in the phosphorus-30 became a neutron, and the element dropped down one notch in the periodic table, from phosphorus (15 protons) to silicon (14 protons). The atomic weight remained the same, 30, because the positron given off had little weight. The silicon was stable, and the reaction ended there.

The Joliot-Curies had discovered the phenomenon they called "artificial radioactivity." By bombarding aluminum with alpha particles, they had turned it first into radioactive phosphorus, then into stable silicon.

At once, atomic scientists began to search for other elements that could be made radioactive artificially.

To understand everything that follows, it must be realized that we will be talking only about changes in the atomic *nucleus.* Thus we will be dealing with the branch of science known as "nuclear physics." The orbiting shells of electrons, which are so important in chemistry, are not involved in the phenomena of nuclear physics.

Since Chadwick's discovery of the neutron in 1932, it has been known that the atomic nucleus consists of two kinds of particles, the positively charged proton and the uncharged neutron. (Hydrogen, of course, has no neutrons—just one proton.) As atoms get heavier, they tend to have more neutrons than protons in their nuclei. Helium has an equal number of neutrons and protons, 2 and 2. The isotope iron-54 has 26 protons and 28 neutrons. Tin has 50 protons and from 62 to 74 neutrons. The isotope lead-208 has 82 protons and 126 neutrons—a neutron surplus of 44. Uranium-238, with 92 protons and 146 neutrons, has 54 extra neutrons.

Mathematically, a neutron can be considered as a proton and an electron joined together. Actually, a neutron does have slightly more mass than a proton. When an atom is jolted by an outside force, the neutron may give off a negative charge with little mass. This is the beta particle. The beta particle is just like an electron, but it comes from the atomic nucleus, not the outer shells.

When a neutron gives off a negative charge, it becomes positively charged. It becomes a proton. So the atom jumps one notch higher in the periodic table, because its atomic number has increased by one.

The proton can give off a small charged particle too. This is the positron. When that happens, the proton loses its charge and becomes a neutron. The atomic number of the element drops by one for each such proton that is changed into a neutron.

Artificial radioactivity and the neutron had been discovered at virtually the same time. It was a happy combination of events. For, as it turned out, the neutron was an excellent "bullet" to use in making elements radioactive artificially. Neutrons readily entered atomic nuclei and became part of them, making them radioactively unstable. One young Italian physicist, Enrico Fermi, saw such great possibilities in artificial radioactivity that he switched from the theoretical side of physics to the experimental at once.

Fermi, who died in 1954, was another of the mighty figures of nuclear physics. Born in 1901, he was in the same age group as Heisenberg, Pauli, Lawrence, Joliot, and many of the others who remade atomic physics in the 1920's and 1930's. They were all born about the turn of the century, and did much of their most important work when they were in their twenties and early thirties.

Fermi was Professor of Theoretical Physics at the University of Rome. No one there had any experience with radioactivity.

The laboratory was poorly equipped. Its budget was so low that Fermi could not use radium in his experiments. At $34,000 a gram, the price was out of the question.

The frail, dark-haired Fermi had never let obstacles of any sort stand in his way. Shy and bookish, he had turned to the study of mathematics and physics after his only brother died, leaving the 14-year-old Fermi without a companion. He went to the University of Pisa, got his degree in 1922, then went to Germany, where the most exciting work in theoretical physics was being done. He was uncomfortable there, and returned to Rome in 1924 to become a teacher of elementary math. That same year he met Laura Capon, who would become his wife four years later, despite the difficulties caused by Laura's being Jewish and Fermi a Roman Catholic.

Laura Fermi described her first meeting with Enrico this way:

"Along with my friends came a short-legged young man in a black suit and black felt hat, with rounded shoulders and a neck craned forward. In Italy a black suit means mourning for a close relative, and I learned that his mother had recently died. His hair was also black and thick, his complexion dark. In introducing him, my friends tried to impress me: 'He is a promising physicist, already teaching at the University, although he is only twenty-two.' "

In 1933, Fermi began his work with neutrons. Unable to afford radium, he used radon, the radioactive gas radium gives off. He mixed radon and beryllium powder in a glass tube; the radon gave off alpha particles that knocked neutrons loose from the beryllium. Since radon's half-life was only four days, Fermi had to make a new neutron "gun" often.

Only with neutrons, Fermi said, could the nuclei of the heavy elements be bombarded. Alpha particles or protons, being positively charged, would be repelled by the heavy, positively charged nuclei. A neutron would not be turned away.

But the neutron posed a different problem. A fast-moving neutron, Fermi discovered, had a tendency to zip right past the nucleus without being captured by it, or else to ricochet away. So even with neutrons, there were few direct hits from the atomic "gun." There were so few that in 1934 Einstein remarked that shooting particles at nuclei was "like shooting birds in the dark in a country where there aren't many birds."

Nevertheless, Fermi set to work. He got samples of every element he could, and bombarded them with neutrons, hoping they would become radioactive as had the aluminum in the Joliot-Curie experiments. He began with hydrogen and worked right up the periodic table. He had no success until fluorine, but then he succeeded in producing a radioactive isotope of fluorine. Quickly, he managed to induce radioactivity in many elements. Iron gave him radioactive manganese; silicon, radioactive aluminum; chlorine, radioactive phosphorus. He turned ordinary sodium into a radioactive isotope of sodium, iodine into radioactive iodine, arsenic into radioactive arsenic.

The alchemy went on. In most cases, the neutron bullet became part of the nucleus it struck, thus creating a new isotope of that element. Generally these isotopes were radioactive. Sometimes the neutron just bounced off the nucleus, though.

In 1934, Fermi and his associates discovered that these bouncing neutrons, which lost speed through their collisions, were captured much more readily by nuclei than ordinary fast-moving neutrons. The discovery was accidental. Fermi noticed that when certain substances were placed between the gun and the target, the number of neutron–nucleus collisions went up sharply. The best substances to use were paraffin and water, he found. It seemed that when the neutrons passed through such substances, which contain a great amount of hydrogen, the hydrogen nuclei—protons—served to slow the neutrons down. The neutrons passed on through, their speed checked, and when they struck the target the chances of a direct hit at a nucleus become much greater.

Certain light elements—hydrogen, beryllium, and carbon particularly—proved to be excellent in slowing down neutrons. Other light elements such as boron were less suitable, because they tended to capture the neutrons permanently instead of just bouncing them around on their way to the target.

Fermi's "slow-moving" technique was a great success. Using a block of paraffin between his neutron source and his target, Fermi was able to slow the neutrons enough to achieve high efficiency in nuclear bombardment. Now he could bombard even the heaviest elements successfully.

In 1934, he attempted a fantastic-sounding experiment. Fermi tried to create a chemical element heavier than uranium! He hoped to induce the nucleus of uranium-238 to capture a neutron. That would make it uranium-239. If a uranium-239 nucleus then gave off a beta particle, one of its neutrons would become a proton, creating a nucleus with 93 protons. That would be a new, man-made element. Since element 93, if he could make it, would be radioactively unstable, it, too, might give off a beta particle and turn into element 94!

So Fermi sent a stream of slow neutrons at a lump of uranium. The result was a mixture of radioactive atoms, difficult to identify. There were four kinds of atoms. One was certainly a new isotope, uranium-239. The others, Fermi thought, might be elements 93, 94, and 95. But he was not sure. When he published his results, he called his paper "Possible Production of Elements of Atomic Number Higher than 92."

The newspapers were not so cautious. *The New York Times,* one of the most careful of newspapers, ran a big headline, "Italian Produces 93rd Element by Bombarding Uranium." Scientists themselves had their doubts. Fermi had produced something, but was it really a group of elements beyond uranium? (Such elements are known as *transuranic* elements.) Laboratories hummed busily in many parts of the world as physicists checked Fermi's findings and tried to duplicate his experiments. Over the next five years, such workers as the Joliot-Curies in France seemed to confirm the Italian's results. But others continued to doubt.

Those five years were years of tension and political turmoil in Europe. In 1933, Hitler had come to power in Germany. He had formed an alliance with Mussolini, the Italian dictator. A persecution of Jews began in Germany, and then spread to Italy a few years later. Enrico Fermi's wife was Jewish. Fermi himself not only feared for his wife's safety but bitterly resented the growing tyranny of the Mussolini government. Late in 1938, Fermi decided to leave Italy and go to some friendlier country. He quietly made arrangements to take up a professorship at Columbia University in New York.

In the middle of these arrangements came word that Fermi had won the 1938 Nobel Physics Prize for his work in slow-neutron reactions. He left Rome with his whole family, and went to Stockholm to collect his award. Then he continued on to the United States. "We have founded the American branch of the Fermi family," he said, as their ship came in sight of New York Harbor and the Statue of Liberty.

While the Fermis were making their way to safety, physicists in another troubled land were still trying to understand what had happened when Fermi bombarded uranium with slow neutrons. A leader in this group was Otto Hahn, of Germany.

Hahn, born in 1879 in Frankfurt, had done his first work in organic chemistry, but soon after the turn of the century became involved, as so many others did, in the study of radioactivity. The year 1905 found him in Montreal, working with Rutherford. Then he returned to Germany to work at the University of Berlin, where he discovered a radioactive substance known as mesothorium—later identified as an isotope of radium.

In 1907, Hahn was joined by an American woman physicist named Lise Meitner, who had come to Berlin from Vienna to attend Max Planck's lectures in physics. She began "temporary" work in Hahn's laboratory, but their association was destined to last 30 years, until interrupted by Nazi terror.

What had begun as a modest laboratory developed into two big departments at the Kaiser Wilhelm Institute of Chemistry —a department of radiochemistry under Hahn, and a department of nuclear physics under Meitner. In 1917, Hahn and Meitner discovered a new element, protactinium. It fit into the periodic table between thorium and uranium, and it was, of course, radioactive.

In 1934, Fermi began his uranium-bombardment experiments. Some scientists thought that one of the radioactive substances produced by Fermi was an isotope of protactinium, rather than a transuranic element. Naturally, this interested Hahn and Meitner, because they knew more about protactinium than anyone else. They began to examine this new substance, which had a half-life of only 13 minutes.

Tests soon showed that Fermi's experiment had not produced protactinium. Nor were his substances isotopes of such other radioactive elements as thorium or actinium. So it did indeed seem possible that Fermi had created element 93, and maybe elements 94 and 95 as well.

Hahn and Meitner continued their work for several years, joined now by another German scientist, Fritz Strassman. They found many radioactive substances not reported in Fermi's original work. They identified one as an isotope of uranium and thought that some of the others were isotopes of element 93. They went on separating the various substances produced by uranium bombardment, and thought they had identified transuranic elements all the way up to atomic number 96. These new elements appeared to have chemical properties similar to known elements lower in the periodic table: rhenium, osmium, iridium, platinum. They formed a series. But in Paris, the Joliot-Curies found what seemed to be yet another transuranic element resembling lanthanum. It did not fit into the Hahn-Meitner-Strassman series at all.

In July, 1938, Lise Meitner had to flee from Germany because of her Jewish ancestry. She went to Sweden, where she joined forces with her nephew, Otto Frisch, who had worked in Niels Bohr's laboratory in Copenhagen. Hahn and Strassman, meanwhile, went on puzzling over the uranium problem.

Late in 1938, Hahn and Strassman were examining one fraction of separated material which they thought consisted of small quantities of radium (element 88), actinium (89), and thorium (90). It was hard to see how radium could have been produced by the neutron bombardment of uranium. For uranium to turn into radium, it had to give off two alpha particles, thus losing four protons. But slow neutrons had never been observed to knock alpha particles out of nuclei. Alpha particles were too massive to be knocked freely by such a slow-moving "bullet."

Then a far more strange problem arose. The sample of radium isotopes turned out, on close examination, to contain some barium. Barium's atomic number was 56! How in the world could the bombardment of a heavy element like uranium produce a middling-heavy element like barium?

Barium and radium have very similar chemical properties, though of course radium is a much heavier element and is radioactive while barium normally is not. When Hahn and Strassman tried to separate their barium from their radium isotopes, they found they could not do it. No chemical process whatsoever would isolate the radioactive barium from the radioactive radium. There was a good reason for this. Hahn and Strassman reported, in 1939, that the "radium" could not be separated from the barium for the simple reason that it *was* barium. "Our 'radium isotopes,' " they wrote, "have the properties of barium and we must really state that in the new substances we are dealing not with radium but with barium." They had also found that one of their "radium" isotopes decayed into lanthanum, element 57—another proof that the parent element was not radium but barium.

The two Germans had kept Lise Meitner and Otto Frisch up to date on their experiments. Hahn and Strassman themselves did not offer an explanation for what had happened. As Hahn wrote, "Our overcautiousness stemmed primarily from the fact that as chemists we hesitated to announce a revolutionary discovery in physics." But Meitner and Frisch, the physicists, gave the explanation of what had taken place in a letter dated January 16, 1939.

All the uranium-bombardment experiments had not simply been adding or substracting a particle or two from the uranium nucleus. They had been splitting it right in half!

The puzzling barium was one of the fragments produced by

this splitting process, which Meitner and Frisch called *nuclear fission*. "It seems possible," they wrote, "that the uranium nucleus has only small stability of form, and may, after neutron capture, divide itself into two nuclei of roughly equal size." In this case, uranium, with an atomic number of 92 and a mass number of 238, had been split into barium (atomic number 56, mass number 138) and krypton (atomic number 36, mass number 83) when struck by a slow neutron. The missing mass had been carried off in the form of energy, according to Einstein's equation. Meitner and Frisch showed how nuclear fission would release a great deal of energy, about 200 million electron volts, because some of uranium's binding energy would be thrown off when the uranium nucleus split into the nuclei of lighter elements.

Frisch hurried to Copenhagen to bring the news to Niels Bohr. It happened that Bohr was about to go to the United States to visit Einstein, who was also a refugee from Nazi persecution. Bohr and Einstein attended a conference of physicists in Washington on January 26, 1939. Fermi was present also. With great excitement the physicists discussed the new phenomenon of fission.

At long last, the puzzle of the transuranic elements was explained. Fermi had found elements which were radioactive and which resembled lighter elements in the periodic table. Since it had never occurred to him or anyone else that an atomic nucleus could be split in half, he did not think that these radioactive elements *were* the lighter elements. He thought they had to be elements higher in atomic number than uranium.

As we will see, such elements have now been produced. But Fermi's element 93, and the other three transuranic elements that Hahn thought he had found, were simply the products of nuclear fission—as was the element the Joliot-Curies had detected. Fermi wrote, "What at that time we thought might be element 93 has proved to be a mixture of decay products. We had suspected it for a long time. Now we are sure of it. We thought that we had a mixture of four elements while their number was closer to fifty."

That riddle had been solved. But a newer, more awesome problem presented itself, that winter day in 1939. Suddenly man had a way of smashing the atom and liberating its fearful energy. Could that energy be put to work somehow? Could its incredible fury be harnessed?

8

THE ATOMIC AGE OPENS

DARK WAR CLOUDS were gathering over Europe. Hitler had seized Austria and Czechoslovakia without a battle, and was looking hungrily toward Poland as 1939 began. Italy was getting ready to attack the small nation of Albania. In the Orient, Japan was already at war with China and casting greedy eyes toward the islands of the Pacific.

In laboratories all over the world, scientists were studying the mysteries of nuclear fission. By the spring of 1939, it was known that uranium atoms had many ways of splitting when struck by neutrons. A uranium atom split into two fragments of only roughly equal size, a heavier fragment and a lighter one. One group of possible fission fragments consisted of elements with mass numbers from 85 to 104. The other group ranged in weight from mass number 130 to 139. However, fission sometimes produced elements with a mass number as low as 72, or as high as 158. Almost 90 kinds of isotopes were found to appear among the fission fragments. And—as well as giving off energy—a fissioning uranium atom also threw off a few free neutrons.

Those free neutrons were all-important to the scientific developments that followed. They have made possible the entire world of atomic energy, both in its destructive and its peaceful applications. For on them depends the vital chain reaction.

Uranium fission, as we have said, gives off about 200 Mev of energy. That is only one-tenth of one percent of the total energy of the uranium nucleus, but it is plenty—for a pound of fissioning uranium could yield as much energy as 10,000 tons of TNT. However it took energy to make fission happen. The scientists had to fire a neutron at a uranium target. Since the energy given off by each uranium atom is actually quite small, there would be no value in fission unless a great many uranium atoms could be made to split all at once. And that would take a great many neutrons. So long as man had to fire those neutrons himself, fission would produce no "profit" of energy.

However, each fissioning uranium atom threw off some extra neutrons itself. If one of those neutrons happened to strike another uranium atom, *it* would fission and throw off neutrons. And those neutrons might strike other uranium atoms, split them, and produce more fission. Thus, a single neutron could touch off a chain of nuclear explosions—a *chain reaction*.

What the world of science wondered, in 1939, was whether such a chain reaction could ever come about.

It depended on how many neutrons were actually produced when uranium fission occurred. Some neutrons were bound to fly off without striking any other atoms. They would be lost to the reaction. Other neutrons might be absorbed by impurities in the uranium, such as boron. They, too, would contribute nothing to a chain reaction. They might even be captured by a uranium nucleus that would refuse to split.

Fermi showed that there would be no chain reaction unless each fissioning nuclei gave off an average of two neutrons apiece. That way, even considering neutron loss, there would be enough neutrons left over to make other uranium atoms split. If one atom gave off two neutrons, and each of them hit a uranium atom and knocked out two more neutrons, there would then be four neutrons bouncing around in the uranium.

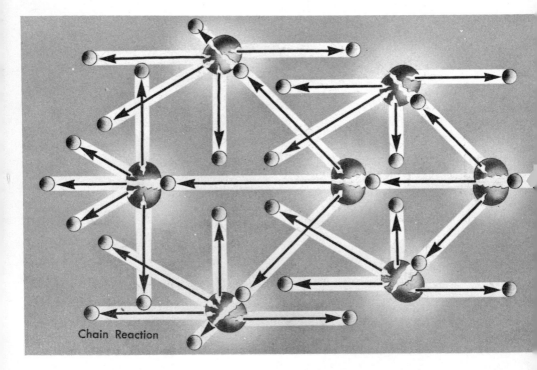

Chain Reaction

If three of them scored direct hits, there would now be six neutrons acting as "bullets." If four or five of them split atoms, eight or ten neutrons would be liberated, and so on and on. There would quickly be so many neutrons in the uranium that the process of fission would continue unstoppably. A huge number of uranium atoms would split and a vast amount of energy would be given off.

Experiments showed that a fissioning uranium atom gave off an average of 2.5 neutrons. Obviously no half neutrons were being produced, so this figure meant that some fissions yielded two neutrons, and some yielded three. At any rate, a chain reaction was theoretically possible.

And Einstein's equation showed how much energy it was possible to get out of such a chain reaction. It was energy that could be put to many uses, if properly controlled. It might wreak frightful destruction, or it might help to turn the earth into a wonderland.

In 1939, the atomic scientists were mostly concerned with the possible destructive uses of that energy. Though the United States was neutral and said it planned to stay that way, most intelligent people realized that eventually we would be drawn into conflict with the forces of evil that had grown so mighty. And when that conflict came, it would be a terrible thing if the enemy had the use of atomic weapons and we did not.

Hahn and Strassman, the discoverers of atomic fission, were still in Hitler's Germany. Other great physicists like Heisenberg were also in Germany. It was altogether possible that Hitler might have ordered every physicist in the country to work on atomic fission for weapons.

So a group of scientists living in the United States got together. Most of them were refugees from Europe, like Fermi, like the Hungarian physicists Leo Szilard and Eugene Wigner, and others. They had seen Nazi tyranny at close range. They decided that the United States government had to be told of the significance of atomic fission.

They went to another refugee, the most famous physicist

of all, Einstein. They wrote a letter which Einstein agreed to sign and take to President Roosevelt. The letter, dated Aug. 2, 1939, said in part:

"In the course of the last four months it has been made probable—through the work of Joliot in France as well as Fermi and Szilard in America—that it may become possible to set up a nuclear chain reaction in a large mass of uranium, by which vast amounts of power and large quantities of new radium-like elements would be generated. Now it appears almost certain that this could be achieved in the immediate future.

"This new phenomenon would also lead to the construction of bombs, and it is conceivable—though much less certain— that extremely powerful bombs of a new type may thus be constructed. . . .

"I understand that Germany has actually stopped the sale of uranium from the Czechoslovakian mines which she has taken over. . . ."

The letter went on to ask the United States to set aside money for nuclear research. It closed with the words, "For the first time in history men will use energy that does not come from the sun."

President Roosevelt was so busy that Einstein could not get to see him for more than two months. Meanwhile, on September 1, Hitler invaded Poland, and Europe was plunged into war, though the United States was not yet involved. On October 11, Einstein brought the letter to the President. Roosevelt set up an Advisory Committee on Uranium, but the only money appropriated was the tiny sum of $6,000. No more funds were granted until October, 1940. And not until December 6, 1941—one day before the Pearl Harbor attack drew the United States into the war—was it decided to make

an all-out effort to master atomic energy. Then the war began
—and men who only a few years before had been busy with
remote and strange theoretical problems suddenly found
themselves trying to build the most terrible weapon in man's
history.

The first step, before any bombs could be built, was to see
if a chain reaction could really be established. That involved
obtaining quantities of a special isotope of uranium.

It had been known for some time that uranium has three
naturally occurring isotopes. The heaviest, uranium-238, is
by far the most common. In nature, uranium-238 makes up
99.282 percent of all the uranium that exists. A lighter isotope,
uranium-235, comprises 0.712 percent of the remaining uranium, and the rest, 0.006 percent, is uranium-234.

Niels Bohr had shown that uranium-238 is less suited for
atomic fission than uranium-235. U-238 has a tendency to
capture slow neutrons and make them part of its nucleus,
instead of fissioning. U-235, on the other hand, fissions easily.
But there is so very little of it in nature—only one atom of
U-235 for every 140 atoms of U-238.

So there had to be some way of assembling large quantities
of the scarce U-235. Then a controlled chain reaction had to
be set up—and, finally, a bomb had to be designed.

The story of the atomic bomb has been told many times.
Since our purpose here is to deal with the theory of the atom,
not with the practical applications of atomic energy, we will
not linger long on the details of the Manhattan Project that
produced the first atomic bombs.

Just about every important physicist in the United States
was involved in the project in one way or another. This included men like Fermi, Szilard, and Wigner; Compton, who

had been so important in the experimental proof of quantum theory; Niels Bohr, who escaped from Nazi-occupied Denmark in 1943, and many others.

Fermi's part in the project was to get a chain reaction going, thus proving that an atomic explosion was possible. He knew that U-238 was a neutron-capturer, and he also knew that slow-moving neutrons were less likely to be captured than fast-moving ones. By slowing down the neutrons, fission would be more readily caused.

Fermi's idea was to mix uranium with some light element that would bounce neutrons around and slow them down. He used graphite, a form of carbon. In 1941, Fermi set up the first structure of the kind later known as an atomic pile or atomic reactor, at Columbia University. It was a cube of graphite about 8 feet on a side, containing 7 tons of uranium oxide distributed at equal intervals. This was not enough to maintain a chain reaction, but it served for experiments.

Fermi placed a small pellet of radium inside a chunk of beryllium the size of a golf ball. The radium gave off alpha particles which knocked neutrons out of the beryllium atoms. Those neutrons entered the atomic pile, rebounded from the nuclei of the carbon atoms, gradually slowed, and eventually fissioned the U-235 atoms in the uranium. Because they were slowed, they were not captured by the U-238.

The first experiments indicated that success lay ahead. Fermi moved on to the University of Chicago, and on November 7, 1942, began to build a full-scale atomic pile in a squash court under the stands of the University's football stadium. (Which, of course, was not being used for football that year!)

Layers of graphite brick were placed on a wooden frame. Then lumps of uranium or uranium oxide were inserted in the pile. There was a very real danger that a chain reaction might start unexpectedly and lead to a catastrophic explosion. To guard against this, the scientists deliberately put strips of a neutron-absorbing element, cadmium, in the pile. The cadmium strips would prevent any chain reaction. They could be drawn out little by little, gradually allowing the activity of build up inside the pile, and could be hastily slammed back into place if things started to get out of hand.

On December 2, 1942, there was enough uranium in the pile to sustain a chain reaction—so the calculations said. About twenty people gathered in the squash court, including Fermi, Szilard, Wigner, and Compton. One man climbed the pile and began to draw the 13-foot-long cadmium control rods out of it, under Fermi's direction. Geiger counters told the scientists that nuclear fission was taking place. At 3:25 in the afternoon, the last control rod was withdrawn. The measuring instruments showed that the chain reaction was self-sustaining. If allowed, it would continue until every uranium atom in the pile had been split. The reaction was under control, so there would be no explosion. Nor would it die out. The pile was delicately adjusted to stay on the tightrope between no fission at all and the sudden, violent destruction of an atomic explosion.

Fermi allowed the reactor to operate for 28 minutes, then ordered the control rods put back in. The celebrating scientists passed around red Italian wine—to honor Fermi— in paper cups. Arthur Compton, who was in charge of providing the uranium supply, put in a long-distance call to Professor James Conant of Harvard, another key member of the scientific team involved in the project. Compton did not dare tell Conant in so many words, "Fermi has achieved a chain reaction." This was wartime, and spies might be listening. Compton's famous words, announcing the dawn of the atomic era, were, "The Italian navigator has just landed in the New World."

"Were the natives friendly?" Conant asked, falling into the spur-of-the-moment code.

"Very," Compton replied.

In Tennessee, a vast new city began to rise between two wooded mountain ridges—Oak Ridge, built by the government. Here, a gigantic plant was established to separate U-235 from U-238. It was all right to use both kinds of uranium in the atomic pile. But that pile had weighed thousands of pounds. A bomb had to be compact—so it had to be made of just the highly fissionable U-235. The Oak Ridge plant separated the two isotopes of uranium by using a gaseous form of uranium, uranium hexafluoride. They pumped this gas through extremely fine sieve-like filters. The gas molecules containing U-235, being lighter, would pass more readily through the filters than the molecules containing U-238, and an elaborate series of barriers would separate the two forms.

But this was not the only way to gather fissionable material. Another method did not have uranium as the end product at all, but rather an artificial transuranic element: plutonium.

Fermi, in 1934, thought he might have discovered a transuranic element. Hahn and Strassman, a few years later, believed they were creating as many as four elements heavier than uranium. But in 1939 Meitner and Frisch showed that these so-called transuranic elements were really only fission products of uranium.

The first real transuranic element was discovered early in 1940 by Edwin McMillan and Philip Abelson at the Radiation Laboratory of the University of California. They bombarded a thin foil of uranium with neutrons. This resulted in atomic fission, but not all the uranium atoms underwent fission. Some of the atoms of U-238 simply captured the neutrons that had been fired at them.

That created a new isotope, U-239. Because such a thin strip of uranium foil had been used, all the radioactive fission products were kicked out of the foil, leaving only the new isotope behind. U-239, they found, had a half-life of 23 minutes. When that time had elapsed, half the U-239 atoms had given off beta particles. By so doing, each U-239 atom effectively gained a proton and jumped up one place in the periodic table—to the hitherto unoccupied 93rd place.

Since Neptune is the planet closest in the heavens to Uranus, the California scientists gave their new element the name of neptunium. It had an atomic number of 93, and a mass number of 239. Its half-life was 2.3 days. Then it gave off a beta particle, which should have resulted in its going up another notch in the table to become element 94. But McMillan and Abelson were unable to find any traces of 94 because they had so little neptunium to work with.

In the same year, another group of California scientists, led by Glenn T. Seaborg, succeeded in finding element 94 by a different route. They bombarded U-238 with a particle called a deuteron, which consists of one proton and one neutron. (We will explain deuterons in a moment.) When a deuteron struck a U-238 nucleus, the nucleus gained a proton, becoming neptunium with its atomic number of 93, and two neutrons escaped. So the atom produced was an isotope of neptunium with the mass number 238. This isotope quickly gave off a beta particle and became element 94, which received the name of plutonium. Plutonium-238 decayed with a half-life of about 90 years, and gave off alpha particles, thus transforming itself back into uranium-238.

Glenn T. Seaborg

Later, it became possible to find the isotope of plutonium that McMillan and Abelson had been looking for, plutonium-239. It had a half-life of 24,400 years. Like U-235, plutonium-239 would undergo fission with slow neutrons. If enough of it could be synthesized, bombs could be made from plutonium.

As for those deuterons: they were first discovered in 1931 by Indiana-born Harold C. Urey (1893–   ), another important scientist who worked on the bomb. Urey, a chemist, took his doctorate at the University of California, where he studied under Gilbert N. Lewis, the man who first put forth the modern theory of electron shells. Lewis had predicted the existence of an isotope of hydrogen that had a mass number of 2 instead of 1—that is, a kind of hydrogen with a neutron as well as a proton in its nucleus. In 1929, after a period of study with Niels Bohr, Urey moved on to Columbia. Two years later, F. G. Brickwedge of the United States Bureau of Standards converted hydrogen gas into a liquid form, evaporated all but a few drops of it, and sent those drops in a sealed glass tube to Urey. Urey examined the sample by passing an electric charge through the tube, and studied the spectral lines that were produced. He was able to identify the heavy isotope of hydrogen, which he called *deuterium*, from the Greek word meaning second. Deuterium's atomic weight is twice that of ordinary hydrogen. There is one atom of deuterium for every 5,000 atoms or so of hydrogen. Later, a third hydrogen isotope with *two* neutrons was discovered, and named *tritium*. Deuterium combines with oxygen to form water just as hydrogen does. Water made of oxygen and deuterium is known as *heavy water*, since its atomic weight is greater than that of ordinary water. The ion of deuterium, consisting of one proton and one neutron, is called a *deuteron*. Deuterons have been used as "bullets" in many atom-smashing experiments.

Could plutonium be mass-produced? At Oak Ridge, a reactor was set up to bombard U-238 with neutrons. That would change the U-238 to U-239, which would quickly become the short-lived neptunium-239 and then plutonium-239. When this method showed promise, much larger reactors were built at a second new "atomic city" in the State of Washington, at Hanford. Meanwhile, yet another group of scientists, under the leadership of J. Robert Oppenheimer (1904–   ) went to New Mexico to work out the design for the atomic bomb itself.

All of this furious and highly secret activity reached its climax early in 1945. The bomb-design problem was to find out how much fissionable material was necessary to bring about the runaway chain reaction known as an atomic explosion. By a series of calculations and some highly dangerous experiments, Oppenheimer's group at the Los Alamos, New Mexico, laboratory found out the minimum size a bomb had to be. This amount of fissionable matter is called a "critical mass." In less than a critical mass, so many neutrons escape that a chain reaction dies down almost as soon as it begins.

Of course, since the so-called "slow neutrons" actually travel quite fast, a critical mass of fissionable matter would explode almost as soon as it was brought together. The bomb had to be designed in such a way that the bomb material was divided in two, and the two pieces did not come together to form a critical mass until the bomb was actually dropped. The scheme worked out involved a kind of gun in which a "bullet" of U-235 or plutonium would be fired at a "target" of the same material when the bomb was dropped.

The Oppenheimer group—which included such celebrated physicists as Chadwick, the discoverer of the neutron, and Niels Bohr—had the first atomic bomb ready for testing at the end of June, 1945. The war in Europe had ended by then, but Japan had not yet surrendered. On July 16, 1945, the Alamogordo Air Base was the scene of the first atomic explosion. The nightmare fury of that explosion awed and stunned the onlookers. The reaction of one of them was quoted in the opening pages of this book.

President Franklin D. Roosevelt had died in April. It fell to the new President, Harry S. Truman, to make the terrible decision to drop the atomic bomb on human beings. With the hope that using the bomb would force Japan to surrender—

thus saving the lives that might be lost if the war dragged on another six months or a year—President Truman gave the order. On August 6, 1945, the city of Hiroshima was destroyed by a single atomic bomb. On Aug. 9, a second Japanese city, Nagasaki, underwent the same devastation, and five days later the war was over. Great Britain's Prime Minister Winston Churchill later estimated that the lives of more than a million American and British soldiers had been saved because the atomic bomb had brought the war to such a quick and dramatic end. And our knowledge of the incredible suffering inflicted on the two Japanese cities has, perhaps, kept us from taking such dreadful weapons lightly. Only five years after the end of World War II, the United States was at war again, in Korea, but no atomic bombs were used in that conflict. Nor have atomic bombs been used anywhere in actual warfare since those two terrible days in August, 1945.

The ugly tensions of the Cold War era, though, have led to the invention of bigger and more frightening bombs. The bombs dropped on Japan had a blast power equal to about 20,000 tons of TNT. Compared to the bombs in arsenals today, those early atomic bombs were nothing more than firecrackers.

The first atomic bombs depended on the fission of plutonium or uranium-235 for their energy. That energy is about 200 Mev per atom. The bomb builders have been able to use the fission explosion to trigger a much greater source of energy —the energy of fusion, rather than fission.

We mentioned before that when the building blocks of an atom—the protons and neutrons—are put together, a certain amount of mass is lost. Of course, the mass is not destroyed, but simply converted into energy.

For instance, a helium nucleus consists of two protons and

two neutrons. The atomic mass of the helium nucleus is slightly less than that of four separate neutrons and protons. The difference, in terms of energy, is 27 Mev. That is the amount given off when two protons and two neutrons are fused together to form one helium nucleus.

The process goes on in the sun all the time, and is the source of the sun's energy. But it does not happen all in one step. In 1938, a Cornell University physics professor, Dr. Hans Bethe, worked out a theory explaining how helium is formed from hydrogen within the blazing furnace of the sun.

Most of the sun's matter is hydrogen. At the fierce temperatures within the sun, this hydrogen is stripped of its electrons —ionized—so that free protons (hydrogen nuclei) swarm in the sun. Bethe showed how a complicated chain of events would bring together two protons, which would give off one positron and become a proton and a neutron, or deuterium. Then these would be struck by another proton to form helium-3; then a fourth proton would join and a second positron be given off, so that the end product would be a helium nucleus. Every second, more than half a billion tons of hydrogen are converted into helium in the sun. Energy is given off —keeping the earth warm—and the sun loses mass, at a rate of 4 million tons a second. Luckily for us, the sun is so immense that it can go on losing mass at that rate for many millions of years without growing cool.

So energy can be obtained from the conversion of hydrogen to helium. But it takes temperatures as hot as the sun's to do the trick. How can man reach such temperatures?

Through atomic fission.

An exploding atomic bomb gives off a great wave of heat, and also a flash of neutrons. The bomb builders put a liner of lithium deuteride in the bomb. This is a compound of the light element lithium and the hydrogen isotope deuterium. When the fission bomb goes off, the neutrons change the lithium to tritium, the other hydrogen isotope. In the intense heat, the deuterium and tritium fuse to form helium, and more energy is given off. The energy of the fusion process, in this case, is only 17.6 Mev per fusion, while it is 200 Mev for each atomic fission. But there are many more atoms in a pound of a light element like lithium than there are in a pound of uranium or plutonium, and so the overall release of energy is greater. In an A-bomb, about one-tenth of one percent of the mass is converted to energy, but in the H-bomb seven-tenths of one percent of the mass is converted to energy.

The bomb builders did not stop there. They wrapped a jacket of uranium around the lithium liner. The jacket consisted mostly of U-238, which normally does not fission when hit by neutrons. But the neutrons given off by the fusion explosion are so fast-moving that they can fission even U-238. So the superbomb operates in three stages. An ordinary atomic bomb triggers the fusion reaction, and the fusion triggers a truly devastating fission explosion. The whole fission–fusion–fission process takes only about a millionth of a second.

The energy released is fantastic. We can talk about A-bombs in terms of thousands of tons of TNT, but the H-bomb's energy is measured in *millions* of tons. A word we have all heard perhaps too often lately is *megaton*, meaning "1 million tons." An H-bomb whose force is equal to that of 2 millon tons of TNT is called a 2-megaton bomb. Both the United States and the Soviet Union have built H-bombs with capacities of many megatons. In October, 1961, the Soviet Union is known to have tested a 50-megaton bomb. This is probably the largest explosion ever made by man.

During the tragically brief administration of President

Kennedy, the United States and Russia agreed to stop testing nuclear bombs, except for certain small underground tests. If this treaty remains in effect, there may never again be an explosion as mighty as that 50-megaton shot of 1961. Since such shots fill the atmosphere with radioactive substances that can harm all living things, let us hope so.

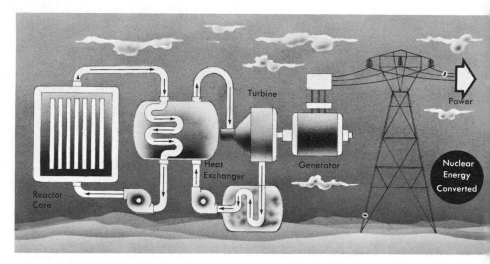

The chain reaction of ideas has brought us a long way since 1930. That was the year that Bothe and Becker produced a beam of neutrons. Then Chadwick identified what they had produced, the Joliot-Curies used neutrons to create artificial radioactivity, and Enrico Fermi went on to bombard uranium with neutrons and produce atomic fission. The work of Hahn, Strassman, Meitner, and Frisch helped to explain what Fermi had really accomplished. And Fermi, Oppenheimer, Compton, Bohr, Urey, and many others, though men of peace and good will, spent some five years perfecting the atomic bomb. What began harmlessly in a German laboratory has ended by putting the power of the sun itself into the hands of mankind.

The same chain reaction that produces explosions can also produce power to run the industries of the world, of course. So the atomic story is not entirely dark and grim. One day the oil and coal that provide so much of today's fuel will all be used up, but there will always be the inexhaustible energy of the atom to keep motors running.

The principle behind an atomic power plant is extremely simple. In a conventional power plant, oil or coal is burned to produce heat that changes water to steam. The steam makes a turbine turn, creating a magnetic field. Faraday, in 1831, had shown how magnets can be used to generate electricity. So the turbine drives the generator, and electric power can be tapped off by power lines. (A turbine can also be turned by the force of water rushing through a dam. This is known as hydro-electric power.)

An atomic power plant works the same way, except that an atomic pile, or reactor, takes the place of the boiler. A controlled chain reaction is started in the pile. Cadmium absorbers keep it in check so there is no danger of a bomb-like explosion. The atomic fission produces heat as a by-product; the heat turns water to steam, and the steam turns the turbine. The electricity thus produced can be used by homes or industry, or can power a ship or a submarine. As nuclear reactors are built to more efficient designs, it becomes cheaper to operate them. Some day in the very near future most of our electrical energy may be produced by atomic reactors.

Of course, even the supply of uranium will be used up one day. But that day seems very far in the future, and long before it comes scientists will have learned how to harness the energy of fusion instead of fission. Right now we can handle fusion energy only in bombs; we can use it to make a big bang, and nothing else. If we could start a fusion reaction, keep it going, and control it, we could tap power from it. The stumbling block is the high temperature fusion generates—hundreds of millions of degrees. Such temperatures would melt any power plant.

For the past decade, scientists have been working on a way to contain and control fusion power magnetically, so that the plasma, or fiercely hot mixture of atomic nuclei and electrons produced by fusion, can be contained without actually touching anything. The work so far is a long way from completion, but that is not to say the problem will not be conquered. *Impossible* is a risky word to use in the field of nuclear physics. "Anyone who looks for a source of power in the transformation of the atoms is talking moonshine," Ernest Rutherford once said. Less than twenty years later, the clicking of a Geiger counter in the squash court at the University of Chicago signaled the beginning of the era of atomic energy.

9

NEW ATOMS FROM OLD

THE EXPERIMENTAL and theoretical sides of atomic research did not come to a halt once practical applications of atomic energy were known. Although today atomics involves engineers as well as physicists and chemists, the work of pure science is more intense than ever. And one of the most fascinating results of modern atomic science has been the creation of a great many elements that do not exist in nature.

We have already seen how neptunium was created artifically by McMillan and Abelson in 1940, and how plutonium was produced in the same year by a group headed by Glenn T. Seaborg. But, though those were the first transuranic elements to be created, they were by no means the first man-made elements.

In the standard periodic table of natural elements, from 1 to 92, four spaces were blank for many years. Elements 43, 61, 85, and 87 had never been detected. After the Joliot-Curies had discovered artificial radioactivity in 1934, scientists wondered if these blank spaces could be filled in the laboratory.

Element 43 was the first target. There was a blank in the table between molybdenum (42) and ruthenium (44). In 1937, a group at the University of California used a cyclotron to hurl deuterons at atoms of molybdenum. They created a radioactive isotope of molybdenum with 42 protons and 57 neutrons. This isotope decayed by throwing off a beta particle, so one neutron became a proton. The result was an element with 43 protons and 56 neutrons—something unknown in nature. The sample was sent to Italy, where two chemists confirmed the discovery. The new element was given the name of technetium, from the Greek *technikos,* "artificial." Technetium-99 has a half-life of almost a million years, and has now been produced in amounts large enough to be studied thoroughly.

Why is there no technetium in nature? Because its half-life is so short that all the technetium present in the earth long since decayed into molybdenum. Unlike the heavier radioactive elements, technetium is not formed as part of a radioactive decay series, so once it was gone, no more was created—until 1937.

Element 85 soon followed. Once again, the alchemy took place at the University of California. The scientists involved were D. R. Corson, K. R. MacKenzie, and Emilio Segrè. (Segrè was one of the two men who had identified technetium in Italy. He had come to California soon after.)

In creating 85, it was not possible simply to add a proton to the next lowest element, as had been done to make 43. In this case, element 84—polonium—was itself extremely rare. The scientists had to go another element down, to 83—bismuth—and add *two* protons. The alpha particle, which has two protons, was used. They bombarded bismuth with alpha particles and obtained an element with 85 protons, which they named astatine, from the Greek word for "unstable."

Astatine is unstable indeed; its most long-lived isotope has a half-life of only a few hours. Then it emits an alpha particle and drops back to being bismuth.

The third of these man-made elements was 61, which is part of the rare-earth group. Rare earths are difficult to analyze, because they resemble each other closely (there are 14 of them) and are hard to separate from one another. Before World War II, some experimenters bombarded rare earths with neutrons in an attempt to produce the missing 61, but the products had such short half-lives that it was impossible to identify them.

During the war, though, new methods for separating the rare earths were devised. Also, it was found that uranium fission produced a long-lived isotope that could definitely be identified as element 61. In 1945, J. A. Marinsky and L. E. Glendenin, at the Oak Ridge National Laboratory, identified the new element and gave it the name of promethium. Prometheus was the Titan of Greek mythology who stole fire from the gods and gave it to man, and 1945 was the year that man had learned the use of a new kind of "fire," atomic energy. The longest-lived isotope of promethium is promethium-147, with a half-life of 3.7 years.

The last gap in the atomic table was filled in 1939 with the discovery of element 87. This element, like the other three, had been hunted by conventional methods for many years, and several times there had been reports of success. But they had all proved to be false alarms. If element 87 existed at all in nature, it had to be in only the most minute trace.

Since all other elements heavier than lead (82) are radioactive, there was good reason to believe that 87 would be radioactive too. Quite possibly it was formed in a decay series starting from one of the heavier elements. By 1914, three separate series were known, one starting with thorium, one with uranium-238, and one with uranium-235. By various steps the series descended toward lead, but each ended in a different though stable isotope of lead.

Element 87 did not fit into any of these three series. But in 1914 three Austrian scientists found that the 89th element, actinium, had two ways of decaying radioactively. Usually it gave off a beta particle, thus rising a notch in the table and becoming the 90th element, thorium. But sometimes actinium gave off an alpha particle. That would drop it two places, to become element 87—otherwise unknown.

Not until 1939, though, did anyone succeed in actually isolating the predicted element. In that year Mlle. M. Perey of France found the alpha-decay product of actinium-227. It was an element with 87 protons and a mass number of 223. She named it francium in honor of her native country. Its half-life was only a few minutes.

Francium can also be produced artifically. When thorium-232 is irradiated with neutrons, it becomes the isotope thorium-233, not found in nature. That isotope decays eventually into francium-221. When the artificial element neptunium was produced, it was found likewise to decay into francium-221. Francium-221 has a half-life of five minutes, and then gives off an alpha particle to become astatine-217, the 85th element. (Which in this case itself breaks down with a half-life of two one-hundredths of a second.)

These four elements completed the periodic table from 1 to 92. The atom-builders did not rest with that achievement. They went on to construct a breathtaking series of transuranic elements—elements with more than 92 protons in their nucleus.

No law of the universe had ever decreed that an atom could have no more than 92 protons. Quite probably, when our world was young, there were many elements heavier than uranium. But their half-lives were short, and eventually they decayed and disappeared completely. Uranium-238, with its half-life of 4.5 billion years, will be present in the earth's crust for billions of years to come, and by its breakdown will go on producing the lighter and shorter-lived radioactive elements. But there was no way, apparently, for uranium to decay upward in the table naturally and turn into an element with a higher atomic number.

Modern science has brought back to life those long-dead heavy elements. Most of the work in producing transuranic elements was done at the University of California, which had the advantage of owning the first cyclotrons ever built. Though many scientists have taken part in the work, the man whose name is most closely associated with the new elements is Glenn T. Seaborg.

Seaborg, formerly Professor of Chemistry at the University of California's Radiation Laboratory at Berkeley, is currently in public life; President Kennedy named him, in 1961, to be chairman of the U. S. Atomic Energy Commission. (The A.E.C. is the five-man board that supervises all of this country's atomic-energy development.) Seaborg took his Ph.D. at Berkeley in 1937, and joined the group trying to create new elements. During World War II, he was part of the atom-bomb project. His particular responsibility was the development of the chemical-separation procedures for the manufacture of plutonium. In 1951, he and E. M. McMillan shared the Nobel Chemistry Prize for their work in creating transuranic elements.

It was McMillan who took part in the synthesis of neptun-

Glenn T. Seaborg

ium, element 93, in 1940. Seaborg led the way toward the discovery of number 94, plutonium, the same year. The need for bomb material led to the development of huge plants to produce plutonium in large quantities. Seaborg and his associates used some of this plutonium, a relatively long-lived radioactive element, to create even heavier artificial elements.

In 1944 and 1945, they added elements 95 and 96 to the list. The first was 96, which was made by bombarding plutonium-239 with alpha particles in a cyclotron. This yielded a new element of mass number 242, with 96 protons in the nucleus, and a half-life of six months. Soon after, the Seaborg group produced element 95 by bombarding plutonium-239 with neutrons. This resulted in the isotope plutonium-241, which was found to decay by giving off a beta particle. That, of course, pushed it up one place in the table to form the 95th element, with a half-life of five hundred years.

These two new elements correspond chemically to two of the rare-earth elements, europium and gadolinium. So the Seaborg group named 95 and 96 in a corresponding way. Europium had been named for Europe, so they called element 95 americium, after America. Gadolinium had been named for a pioneering chemist called Gadolin, so element 96 was given the name of curium, in honor of those other great scientists, the Curies.

Element 97 joined the roll late in 1949. The starting point was americium, which the Berkeley experimenters produced in tiny amounts smaller than the point of a needle. Using their cyclotron, they accelerated alpha particles to 35 Mev and fired them at the americium nuclei. The new element, with 97 protons, had a mass number of 243 and a half-life of less than five hours. Since the corresponding rare-earth element had been named for the city where it was first discovered, Seaborg gave element 97 its name the same way: berkelium. By now, several isotopes of berkelium with half-lives of thousands of years have been produced.

High-speed alpha particles also gave the California scientists the 98th element, a few months later. They hurled the alpha particles at curium, raising its atomic number from 96 to 98. One neutron was thrown off in this reaction. The new element, with a mass number of 245, had a half-life of only 44 minutes, and the first experiments produced a mere 5,000 atoms. Later, a way was found to produce another isotope of element 98 by using bigger "bullets." A powerful accelerator was used to throw ions of carbon-12 (6 protons, 6 neutrons) at uranium-238. That raised the atomic number of the nucleus from 92 to 98. Elements 97 and 98 were also synthesized by causing plutonium, americium, and curium to capture several neutrons apiece in successive bombardments, after which they gave off beta particles.

The rare-earth "cousin" of element 98 is dysprosium, whose name comes from a Greek word meaning "difficult to get at." Seaborg's group decided to name their newest element californium, explaining that at one time California, too, had been "difficult to get at," when another element was sought—gold.

Elements 99 and 100 were not originally laboratory products. They were discovered quite by accident. The first hydrogen bomb had been exploded in a test on a Pacific island, on November 1, 1952. Airplanes flying by remote control were sent through the explosion cloud to pick up radioactive material on filter paper. This was sent back to the United States for analysis.

It was found that the H-bomb explosion had created some new heavy isotopes of plutonium. This led the Berkeley people to suspect that the shot—man's biggest explosion up to that time—might have created other new chemical substances. They asked for more material to examine, and were given several hundred pounds of coral from a nearby island that had been made radioactive by the explosion.

Examining the coral, they found traces of two new elements. Element 100, for instance, was identified on the basis of only some 200 atoms. It was given the name of fermium, in honor of Enrico Fermi. Element 99 was named einsteinium, after Albert Einstein.

The H-bomb had created the two new elements by subjecting uranium to a heavy bombardment of neutrons. After the discovery of einsteinium and fermium, the A.E.C. laboratories at Arco, Idaho, were able to produce the elements synthetically by bombarding plutonium with neutrons in an atomic reactor.

The plutonium captured neutron after neutron, eventually building up to element 100 as the neutrons gave off beta particles and became protons. It takes two or three years to turn plutonium into fermium this way. An H-bomb does the job in a millionth of a second.

Einsteinium and fermium could be produced only in extremely minute quantities, and the two elements in their various isotopes had half-lives of a few months at best. That led Seaborg to write in 1956, "It appears that einsteinium is the heaviest element it will be possible to isolate in visible quantities."

But by that time he had already gone on to discover element 101. It was a seemingly impossible task. Seaborg felt that the best way to try it was to bombard element 99, einsteinium, with alpha particles. But all the einsteinium available amounted to only a billion atoms, which may sound like a lot but which is actually not very much at all. The Berkeley scientists calculated that if they bombarded their billion atoms of einsteinium for several hours with a high-intensity alpha-particle beam, they would produce *one* atom of element 101!

And that one atom, they also calculated, would have a half-life of ten minutes. So they would have almost no time at all to find their atom of 101 among the billion atoms of einsteinium. Put that way, a billion atoms is a great many indeed.

They tried it. They spread their tiny supply of einsteinium on a strip of gold foil. If the alpha particles, striking the einsteinium, attached themselves to the einsteinium nuclei, the impact would jolt the combined atoms off the foil and onto a second gold foil nearby. The new element then might possibly be isolated by chemical means.

It proved impossible to isolate element 101 chemically. The experimenters next tried to identify the new element by measuring the intensity with which it threw off alpha particles. They were able to calculate in advance the intensity that they could expect. The trouble was, though, that radon, the radioactive gas, releases alpha particles at about the same energy as that expected for 101. So even if they detected the alpha emission, they could not be sure that 101 was responsible; it might have been radon.

In any case, *no* alpha particles were given off. Something else happened. The atom of element 101 gave off a positron and became an isotope of element 100, fermium. Fermium could be detected. So the experimenters now had to look for instances when the alpha-particle bombardment of einsteinium produced fermium, which it could do only by first producing element 101. They rigged up a counting circuit to record each such atomic event. Seaborg writes, "On the average it was possible to make only one of these new atoms in each experiment: sometimes there were two, sometimes none. A huge fire bell in the hall of the chemistry building was connected to the counting circuit, so that each of these rare events pealed a loud clang of rejoicing. But this sport was put to a justifiable end when it came to the attention of the fire department."

On the basis of just one or two atoms, it was possible to arrive at an exact chemical identification of the new element. It was named mendelevium, after Mendeleev, the first to devise a workable periodic table of the elements. Since the original experiments, a greater quantity of einsteinium had become available, and it was possible to produce more than 100 atoms of mendelevium at a time. The half-life of mendelevium-256 turned out to be about an hour and a half.

The Californians had had a hand in the synthesis of all nine transuranic elements thus far. So it seemed a little strange when the announcement of element 102 came from a different laboratory. The Nobel Institute for Physics in Stockholm, Sweden, let it be known in July, 1957, that an isotope of element 102 had been produced by bombarding curium-244 with the nuclei of carbon-13. This new element, named nobelium after Alfred Nobel, whose will had established the Nobel prize, had a half-life of about ten minutes. It decayed by throwing off alpha particles at high energy.

Scientists in other parts of the world were puzzled. It did not seem possible that an atom which emitted alpha particles so intensely (at an energy of 8.5 Mev) could have a half-life even as long as ten minutes. At many laboratories in the United States and in Russia, attempts were made to produce nobelium, using instruments more sensitive than those employed at Stockholm. No one could duplicate the Stockholm work. It finally was concluded that the Swedish experimenters had been premature. Whatever they had produced, it had not really been element 102. The name "nobelium" was wiped from the list.

Then, in April, 1958, the real 102 finally was discovered. Once again, the work was done at Berkeley. A new, powerful accelerator called HILAC (Heavy-Ion Linear Accelerator) had gone into operation there, capable of accelerating nuclei heavier than alpha particles. The Berkeley researchers bombarded curium-246 with the nuclei of carbon-12. The 6 protons in the carbon nucleus combined with the 96 of curium to produce a nucleus of 102 protons. The half-life of element 102 is about three seconds, and then it gives off an alpha particle to become fermium-250. That in turn decays with a half-life of thirty minutes, also giving off an alpha particle and becoming californium.

The new element has not yet been named. Since the discoverers of an element have the right to name it, the eventual name will probably not be the discarded "nobelium." Because its half-life is so short and so few atoms can be produced, element 102 has not been identified chemically. Its existence is known from the element into which it decays. When the scientists see that an alpha particle has been given off, and find an atom of fermium, they know that an atom of 102 has been there—and gone.

Element 103, first discovered in the spring of 1961, is another quick vanisher. It was produced—yes, at Berkeley—by using the HILAC to bombard californium with boron nuclei. The 5 protons of the boron joined with the 98 protons of californium to create an element with 103 protons. It has been named lawrencium, in honor of Ernest O. Lawrence, the inventor of the cyclotron. Its half-life is eight seconds, and it decays by violently throwing off an alpha particle.

So far as Berkeley is concerned, the story of the transuranic elements stops with lawrencium. Since 1961, the California physicists had attempted to produce element 104 by bombarding californium with carbon nuclei in the HILAC. But in August, 1964, before they had achieved success, news came that a Soviet team had got there first.

The Russian announcement came from Prof. Dmitri Blokhintsev, director of the Joint Nuclear Research Institute in Dubna. He said that a group headed by Dr. Georgi Flerov had created the newest element by hitting a plutonium target with accelerated ions of neon. Plutonium's atomic number is 94, that of neon 10—giving the new element the atomic number of 104. Its half-life, the Russians said, was about three-tenths of a second, and so far only about 150 atoms of 104 had been created. They did not immediately offer a name for the new element.

The discovery, as of late 1964, remained uncertain. Berkeley scientists no doubt will attempt to duplicate the Russian work. Perhaps Dr. Flerov and his co-workers will be proven correct,, in which case Berkeley's long monopoly on new elements will be broken. Or possibly "element 104" will go the way of "nobelium."

Since the most recent elements have had half-lives of only a few seconds, Glenn Seaborg thinks that it will be difficult to continue atom-building much further. He wrote in 1963, "It will apparently not be possible to synthesize and detect new elements beyond about element 110, and the study of their chemical properties may become impossible long before this atomic number is reached."

However, research is producing new isotopes of the transuranic elements already known. Some of these isotopes have very long half-lives. So while the first isotope of curium that was produced had a half-life of 6 months, a recently produced curium isotope has a half-life of half a million years—long enough so that many experiments can be done with it. A long-lived form of einsteinium has now been synthesized also. Altogether, there are about 100 known isotopes of the eleven transuranic elements created through the end of 1963, not counting the Russian-discovered element 104.

It is fair to ask some questions at this point: Why bother making transuranic elements? What good are they? Is it done just as a sort of clever game, like playing chess or doing crossword puzzles? Are the Berkeley scientists simply showing how smart they are?

One reason for making transuranic elements is, of course, the importance of knowledge for its own sake. The more that science knows about atoms, the better, from a purely scientific point of view. We can never have too much understanding of the universe. Creating transuranic elements has helped to bring new insight into the nature of the atom and into the workings of that still mysterious process, radioactivity. Science still has no real explanation for the spontaneous breakdown of certain atoms. We know that some heavy atoms, and a few light ones, shoot off alpha particles or beta particles of their own accord, changing into other atoms. But we do not yet know *why*. Perhaps the transuranic research will someday tell us that.

There are also good, sound, practical uses for the transuranic elements. We have already seen how the only naturally occurring substance suited for use in atomic reactors (or atomic bombs) is uranium-235. This is quite a rare isotope. If we had to depend on U-235 alone for atomic power, all the nuclear fuel in the world would swiftly be used up. But we have learned how to turn uranium-238, which is not useful for atomic energy, into the transuranic element plutonium-239. Because we know how to make plutonium, our supply of atomic fuel has been increased many times over. In decades to come, plutonium will be a steadily more important source of atomic power.

Plutonium-238, a lighter isotope, has the property of giving off heat without fissioning. Curium-242 and curium-244 also have this property. They give off alpha particles which are converted into heat when stopped by a surrounding mass. The new field of thermoelectricity has found ways to convert this heat directly into electricity, without generators having moving parts. The space satellite Transit IV-A, launched in 1961, contained a thermoelectric power source that used plutonium-238. Such heavier elements as californium-252 and californium-254 may also have practical applications in research and industry, according to Glenn Seaborg.

So the making of new elements is more than just an intellectual game. It is a modern kind of alchemy that has already produced real usefulness, as well as new theoretical knowledge.

THE TRANSURANIC ELEMENTS

ATOMIC NUMBER	NAME	YEAR OF DISCOVERY	HOW FIRST PREPARED	HALF-LIFE OF FIRST ISOTOPE IDENTIFIED
93	Neptunium	1940	Bombardment of uranium-238 with neutrons	2.35 days
94	Plutonium	1940	Bombardment of uranium-238 with deuterons	86.4 years
95	Americium	1945	Bombardment of plutonium-239 with neutrons	458 years
96	Curium	1944	Bombardment of plutonium-239 with alpha particles	162.5 days
97	Berkelium	1949	Bombardment of americium-241 with alpha particles	4.5 hours
98	Californium	1950	Bombardment of curium-242 with alpha particles	44 minutes
99	Einsteinium	1952	Bombardment of uranium-238 with neutrons in first H-Bomb explosion	20 days
100	Fermium	1953	Bombardment of uranium-238 with neutrons in first H-Bomb explosion	22 hours
101	Mendelevium	1955	Bombardment of einsteinium-253 with alpha particles	1.5 hours
102	?	1958	Bombardment of curium-246 with carbon ions	3 seconds
103	Lawrencium	1961	Bombardment of californium-252 with boron ions	8 seconds
104	?	1964	Bombardment of plutonium-239 with neon-22 ions	0.3 second

10

PARTICLES AND MORE PARTICLES

W HEN CHADWICK discovered the neutron in 1932, it seemed to complete the list of the atom's building blocks. First the tiny, negatively charged electron had been found; then, the larger, positively charged proton. And, finally, the uncharged neutron. Protons and neutrons made up the nucleus, and electrons revolved around them. It was neat and logical.

And incomplete.

Back at the turn of the century, when Roentgen and Becquerel and the Curies were experimenting, the world of science had to make sense out of rays and yet more rays. Eventually, all the new kinds of radiation were explained and labeled. Since the middle of the 1930's, scientists have been trying to do the same with the so-called "elementary" particles. In 1932 there were just three such particles—the electron, the proton, and the neutron—plus a fourth, the photon or quantum of energy, that is not always grouped with the other three. As of the 1960's, more than *30* elementary particles have been discovered. One of the biggest problems of physics today is to explain where all those particles come from and what their functions are.

For everyday purposes, the electron–proton–neutron trio is still the most important. Those three particles are the main building blocks of the atom, even in today's thinking. Chemical reactions are still explained in terms of what happens to electrons in an atom's outer shell. Atomic number is still figured from the number of protons alone. The mass number is still the sum of the protons and neutrons in the nucleus.

What are all the new particles, then?

Many of them, we think, have something to do with the binding forces that hold the nucleus together. More than fifty years ago, Ernest Rutherford wrote these words, which we have already quoted: "It would appear as if the positively charged atoms of matter attract one another at very small distances, for otherwise it is difficult to see how the component parts at the center are held together."

The ranks of new particles have also been swollen by the discovery of the so-called *antiparticles*. These are the exact opposites of more familiar particles.

The positron, which was the first of the new particles to be discovered, is such an antiparticle. We have already mentioned how Carl D. Anderson discovered the positron in 1932 while examining the photographs of cosmic-ray collisions. P. A. M. Dirac had worked out equations that required the existence of both positive and negative electrons. Anderson found the track of a positive electron. Its mass, like that of the electron, was only about 1/1,840th that of a proton. But its charge was positive.

Positrons are formed, as already noted, when high-energy photons such as gamma rays or X rays collide with matter. The

photons, which represent energy, are converted into mass—
each photon becoming an electron–positron pair. The negative charge of the electron balances out the positive charge of
the positron, so no new charge has really been created. Like all
antiparticles, positrons seek out their opposites—electrons, in
this case—and they annihilate each other. A photon is formed
when such collisions take place.

The positron, surprising particle that it was, served an
important mathematical purpose in the scheme of things.
Without it, there would be no way of explaining where the
negative charge came from when gamma rays became electrons.
The discovery that a positive charge was created at the same
time left everything neatly balanced.

The next new particle also was conjured up by a theoretical
physicist to explain a puzzle. While a neutron remains inside
the nucleus, it is extremely stable, except in radioactive atoms.
We have seen that neutrons in radioactive atoms can emit beta
particles—electrons—and turn into protons.

A neutron that is separated from the atomic nucleus will also
emit a beta particle. Such free neutrons are unstable. In an
average time of 18 minutes, such a neutron will decay into a
proton by giving off a beta particle. But the mathematics of
the situation did not make sense to the men who calculated
the effect. For one thing, the neutron before decay was about
1.5 electron masses heavier than the proton and electron it
decayed into. In terms of energy, this was some 780,000 electron volts. Where did the missing energy (or mass) go? If it
just disappeared, the law of conservation of energy was in
error—a frightening thought to a scientist.

There was also the problem of missing spin. All known
atomic particles had been found to spin like tops. The amount
of this spin could be measured. A special unit of spin was
established. An electron, a positron, a proton, and a neutron

each had a spin of ½. It was agreed that in any nuclear reaction, spin—like matter, energy, or electric charge—could be neither lost nor created. This was known as the law of conservation of angular momentum, which is another phrase for "spin."

The breakdown of a neutron—which is called *beta decay*— seemed to violate the law of conservation of angular momentum. A neutron, with a spin of ½, decayed into a proton and an electron, *each* with a spin of ½. An extra spin of ½ had been created, seemingly. Or, if the proton and electron had opposite spins which balanced out, half a unit had been lost. How could this be explained? Either way, the law of conservation of angular momentum seemed violated.

It was unthinkable that two important conservation laws like that of energy and of angular momentum had to be thrown out. So, in 1933, Wolfgang Pauli did something that looked very much like cheating. He invented a particle that no one had ever seen. It had no electric charge, and not even any mass while at rest. But it had a spin of ½. During beta decay, Pauli said, this ghostly particle was emitted by the neutron along with the beta particle. The missing 780,000 electron volts of energy were carried off by this newly suggested particle. And its spin of ½ cancelled out the spin of one of the other particles, leaving a total spin of ½ in the system, the same that the neutron had had originally.

It was a very pretty theory. And it saved the laws of conservation. Physicists everywhere heaved sighs of relief. Enrico Fermi gave the new particle a name: *neutrino*, meaning "little neutral one." Once again, the mathematics of the atom made sense.

Of course, there was one nagging little difficulty. Until someone produced experimental evidence that neutrinos really existed, no one could totally trust the laws of conservation of energy and angular momentum. Suppose Pauli was wrong; suppose there was no neutrino, and energy and angular momentum were *not* conserved in beta decay? Frightful thought!

So scientists went looking for the neutrino. But how do you find a particle that has no charge and no mass? If neutrinos existed at all, there could not be many of them. Beta decay is a rare event in the atomic world—it hardly ever happens. So the reverse event—the capture of a neutrino by a nucleus— had to be just as rare. It was calculated that a neutrino would have to pass through a wall of lead as thick as 100 million stars before it was likely to be captured by a nucleus.

The development of atomic reactors, though, made great masses of artificially radioactive substances available to experimenters. In theory, it was felt, an atomic reactor should give off a great many neutrinos. Possibly one might be detected, and the long uncertainty ended.

The quest lasted almost a quarter of a century. In the summer of 1956, two members of the Los Alamos Scientific Laboratory, Frederick Reines and Clyde L. Cowan, Jr., found the neutrino. They did their work at what was then the biggest nuclear reactor in the United States—the Savannah River pile. "Seeing" a neutrino itself was impossible, of course. But they set out to detect the reverse of beta decay: the capture of a neutrino by a proton, which would then turn into a neutron and a positron.

They set up two tanks of water about 6 feet long, $4\frac{1}{2}$ feet wide, and 3 inches thick. The water contained hydrogen nuclei—protons. The water tanks were sandwiched among three other tanks containing a fluid that would produce a flash of light every time a positron and an electron annihilated each other.

The idea was that neutrinos would stream into the tank from the reactor. Some of them might be captured by protons. Positrons would be given off, they would collide with the nearest electrons, and the scintillating fluid would flash. The neutron formed at the same time would be captured almost at once by the nucleus of a cadmium atom (cadmium was dissolved in the target water) and that would cause flashes of light too. Electronic recorders would measure and count the flashes.

Reines and Cowan ran their experiment for 1,371 hours. They got flashes just when they expected them. Neutrinos were captured at a rate of one or two an hour. When the power of the reactor was stepped up, the pace of the flashes increased also, showing that neutrinos were really being given off.

So the existence of the neutrino has been experimentally proved. Like the positron, it was predicted mathematically first, detected later. We still do not know what purpose the neutrino serves in the structure of atoms. Since it has no charge and no mass while at rest, it really does not exist at all until a neutron decays. Then it flies off—carrying with it part of the neutron's energy.

The next particle added to the list was also predicted in advance. In 1932, after the neutron was discovered, Werner Heisenberg offered a theory that could explain what held the nucleus together. He suggested that protons and neutrons in the nucleus constantly tossed back and forth a charged particle, billions of times a second. In this game of cosmic "catch," whichever one had the charged particle at the moment was the proton. And the back-and-forth shuttle of the charge somehow kept the nucleus from flying apart.

When the positron was discovered soon afterward, some

physicists suggested that this was the particle Heisenberg had been talking about. But the positron was too light. It did not have enough mass to fit the mathematical calculations.

In 1935, the Japanese theoretician, Hideki Yukawa, put forth the idea that this particle, if it existed, was smaller than a proton, but about 200 times as massive as an electron. He pictured it as a kind of field within the atom, which represented the binding energy of the nucleus. If it could be transformed into mass and separated from the nucleus, it would have a very short life-span, dying in a millionth of a second. Yukawa gave this hypothetical particle the name of *meson*. To account for the bond between proton and proton, proton and neutron, and neutron and neutron, he said there would have to be positive, negative, and neutral mesons.

The meson remained just a theory until 1937. In that year, a group of investigators led by Carl Anderson, studying the atomic debris produced by cosmic rays, found the tracks of particles about 200 times the mass of an electron. Was this Yukawa's meson?

In seemed to be—except for one thing. The theory said that mesons should be absorbed readily by atomic nuclei. These particles hardly ever seemed to interact with nuclei at all.

The 1937 particle remained a puzzle for a full ten years. Then Robert E. Marshak of the University of Rochester put forth a solution. There were, he said, *two* kinds of meson. One was a heavier kind which obeyed Yukawa's predictions. The other was a lighter meson into which the heavier one decayed. The mesons observed in the cosmic-ray photos, Marshak said, were of the lighter kind.

The trouble, according to Marshak, was that mesons were knocked out of atoms by cosmic rays high in the atmosphere. In a hundred-millionth of a second, the heavy meson decayed into the light meson. That gave it no time to fall far into the atmosphere. But if photographs could be taken at high altitudes, it might be possible to catch the track of the heavy meson before it decayed.

Almost at once, the heavy meson was found. Scientists in the Bolivian Andes took photographs at extremely high altitudes, and they showed meson tracks. Soon after, at the University of California, the Berkeley cyclotron was used to knock mesons out of nuclei by alpha-particle bombardment.

The heavy meson, which fits Yukawa's predictions exactly, is now called the *pi* meson (mesons are identified by Greek letters). Pi mesons come in three varieties—positive, negative, and neutral. The pi mesons have a mass about 270 times that of an electron. The lighter mesons are called *mu* mesons. Their mass is about 200 times that of an electron. Only two forms of mu mesons have been found, the positive and the negative. The neutral mu meson, if it exists at all, would be as hard to detect as a neutrino.

Pi mesons are usually referred to now as *pions*, mu mesons as *muons*. A positive pion decays into a positive muon and a neutrino. A negative pion decays into a negative muon and an antineutrino. (The antineutrino is to the neutrino as the positron is to the electron. Antineutrinos spin the opposite way from neutrinos.) Neutral pions decay into protons and antiprotons (yes, another antiparticle, which we'll come to later.)

All these reactions happen unimaginably fast—in a fraction of a billionth of a second. Nor do the decay products last long, either. The positive muon decays almost at once into a positron, a neutrino, and an antineutrino. The negative muon breaks down into an electron, a neutrino, and an antineutrino.

The story is suddenly very complicated. By about 1950, a

host of new particles had come to join the photon, the electron, the proton, and the neutron. There was the neutrino and its antiparticle. There was the pi meson in its three forms. There was the mu meson in its two forms. There was the positron, and later the antiproton and even the antineutron.

Confusion? It was just beginning!

The antiproton joined the list in 1955. It was already known, in theory, that every basic particle had its own opposite particle. Physicists were searching for a particle with the mass of a proton, but with a negative charge. Such a particle, when it collided with a proton, would release a great deal of energy—much more than when a positron and an electron collide.

A group of scientists at the University of California, led by Emilio Segrè and Owen Chamberlain, set out to create antiprotons in the laboratory and thus demonstrate their existence. They planned to do this by hurling protons against other protons with great energy. The collision of proton and proton, if violent enough, would transform energy into mass and result in the creation of a proton–antiproton pair.

But vast energy was needed. The energy equivalent to the mass of one proton is about a billion electron volts. So at least 2 Bev would be needed to make a proton–antiproton pair. It proved necessary to accelerate protons to a 6-Bev energy. This was accomplished in the bevatron, the University of California's powerful particle accelerator. Protons were fired with 6-Bev energy at a target of copper.

The collision generated not only antiprotons but a great many mesons—40,000 mesons for each antiproton. But mesons, being lighter, travel faster than antiprotons. The experimenters built detectors sensitive enough to measure differences of a billionth of a second as the particles covered a 40-foot track. It took the anti-protons 51 billionths of a second to travel the 40 feet, while the mesons made the journey in just 40 billionths of a second!

The bevatron created about four antiprotons an hour. When an antiproton met a proton or a neutron, the violent meeting showed up as an "annihilation star" on a photographic plate. The two particles broke into a shower of fragments.

The antiproton was an expected particle. It fit into the symmetrical scheme of things. On the other hand, the mu meson did not fit at all. Why should pions decay into slightly lighter particles? What role did the muon play?

No one knew. But the muon was the first in a steady procession of mysterious particles. In 1948, two English scientists doing cloud-chamber work discovered peculiar V-shaped tracks left behind after cosmic rays had struck a lead plate in the cloud chamber. At first there was no way to account for these unfamiliar-looking tracks. It was suggested that some unknown neutral particle was set free when the high-energy cosmic rays struck. This neutral particle left no track of its own, but speedily decayed into two charged particles that formed the V-shaped track.

Soon the troublesome neutral particles were pinpointed. There were two of them, both heavy. One—called the lambda particle—decayed into a proton and a negative pion, and had a mass 2,181 times that of the electron. The other—called the K particle—decayed into a positive pion and a negative pion, and had a mass of 965 electron masses.

Others followed with bewildering rapidity. There came the sigma particles—positive, negative, and neutral—and the negative xi particle, and then the positive and negative K particles, to go with the neutral one already known. All these particles had lifetimes ranging from a 10 millionth to a 10 billionth of a second. Then they decayed into other, more familiar particles.

What was surprising was not that their life-spans were so short, but that they were so long! It was calculated that a lambda particle was formed by the collision of a proton and a negative pion in 1/100,000,000,000,000,000,000,000th of a second. The lambda should break down into the same two particles at the same incredible speed—that is, the death of a lambda should happen as fast as the birth of a lambda. That is how things usually work within the atom; a reaction takes the same time no matter which direction it is going. But the lambda lived an astonishingly long time, by atomic standards —100,000 billion times as long as it should!

Another basic law of nuclear physics was in danger. Then it was shown that the creation of lambdas did not really have to be exactly reversible in time span. A complicated explanation saved the system.

We do not need to go into further details about these strange particles, because we have come almost up to date in the world of nuclear physics, and anything written now would be out of date in a few months. Events move fast on any frontier. Particle follows particle, and the list grows rapidly—and may go on growing. In August, 1963, the 34th elementary particle was discovered by a team of 13 physicists from Yale University and the Brookhaven National Laboratory. They gave it the name of the anti-xi-zero. It is the antiparticle of the xi-zero particle, which was discovered in 1959. Physicists no longer spend much time with the comfortable, familiar particles like protons and electrons. They must cope with these bizarre, strangely named new particles set free by high-energy impacts.

The list, as of the end of 1964, looks like this:

There are the 4 "old" particles and their antiparticles—

the photon, the electron, the neutron, and the proton. That adds up to 8. There are 2 kinds of neutrinos, one associated with muons and the other with electrons, and they have corresponding antiparticles. Thus, 4 more. Then there is the neutral pi meson and its antiparticle, and the positive pi meson and *its* antiparticle, which of course is the negative pi meson. Another 4 there. Then the positive mu meson and its antiparticle, the negative mu meson. Another 2. That gives us 18 particles to here.

Now we enter the realm of what physicists call the "strange" particles. The lambda and the antilambda, the neutral K particle and the neutral anti-K—4 particles there. The positive and negative K particles are 2 more. Then there are positive, negative, and neutral sigma particles and an antiparticle for each. Chalk up another 6! Then the xi-zero particle and the anti-xi-zero particle, and the positive xi particle and the negative xi particle—4 more! There are thus 16 strange particles in all, making 34 "elementary" particles.

And it doesn't stop there. At the moment, there are a dozen other particles called "resonance particles," which have lifetimes of a hundred-thousandth of a billion-billionth of a second, and which are considered in a "family" separate from the first 34 particles.

The welter of new particles is the despair of scientists as well as laymen. Within about ten years, nuclear physics has been thrown into complete chaos. Though the old relationships among electrons, protons, and neutrons, which we have traced all through this book, still hold true, the new particles pose more puzzles than most physicists care to think about.

At a meeting held at the University of California in October, 1963, a group of nuclear physicists tried to bring order out of the chaos. One of them, Dr. Geoffrey F. Chew of Berkeley, suggested that there might be an almost limitless number of new heavy particles. But he held out hope that with the development of more powerful atom-smashing machines, further experiments might succeed in making the meaning of the new particles clear.

So we must drop the discussion of atomic particles on a note of doubt, mystery, and confusion. We who are not nuclear physicists can understand atoms quite successfully if we simply think of them as made up of electrons, protons, and neutrons, with pi mesons binding their nuclei together, and positrons and neutrinos given off at certain times under special circumstances. We can happily leave the rest of the story to the atomic scientists themselves, and allow them to puzzle through their jumble of lambdas and sigmas without us. Perhaps someday soon, one of them will be able to tell the world what the new particles really are, just as one day long ago Ernest Rutherford was able to explain what the alpha, beta, and gamma rays were.

The atomic story is really just beginning. The whole era of atomic science so far, from Roentgen's X rays through the atomic bomb to the lambda and xi and sigma particles, has been only a prelude. The quest of the scientist must always be endless. For mystery lies beyond mystery, and we move step by step into the unknown, with greater riddles everlastingly in wait to test the mind of man.

Books marked (*) are particularly recommended for young readers.

* Asimov, Isaac, *Inside the Atom*. New York: Abelard-Schuman, 1960.

Bohr, Niels, *Atomic Physics and Human Knowledge*. New York: John Wiley, 1958.

* Dietz, David, *Atomic Science, Bombs and Power*. New York: Dodd Mead, 1954.

* Hecht, Selig, *Explaining the Atom*. New York: Viking, 1959.

* Jaffe, Bernard, *Men of Science in America*. (Chapter on Ernest O. Lawrence.) New York: Simon and Schuster, 1944.

Lapp, Ralph, *Atoms and People*. New York: Harper, 1956.

* ———, *Roads to Discovery*. New York: Harper, 1960.

Laurence, William L., *Men and Atoms*. New York: Simon and Schuster, 1959.

Lucretius, *De Rerum Natura (The Nature of the Universe.)* Translated by R. E. Latham. Harmondsworth, England: Penguin Books, 1951.

* McKown, Robin, *The Fabulous Isotopes*. New York: Holiday House, 1962.

Moulton, F. R., and Schifferes, J. J. (eds.), *The Autobiography of Science*. New York: Doubleday, 1945.

Nahm, Milton C., (ed.), *Selections From Early Greek Philosophy*. New York: Appleton-Century Crofts, 1947.

Newman, James R. (ed.), *The World of Mathematics*. New York: Simon & Schuster, 1956.

* Pearl, Carleton. *The Tenth Wonder, Atomic Energy*. Boston: Little, Brown, 1956.

Reichenbach, Hans, *Atom and Cosmos*. New York: Braziller, 1957.

* Riedman, Sarah R., *Men and Women Behind the Atom*. New York: Abelard-Schuman, 1958.

Sarton, George, *A History of Science*. Cambridge: Harvard University Press, 1952, 1959.

Seaborg, Glenn T., *The Transuranium Elements*. New Haven: Yale University Press, 1958.

Shapley, Harlow, Rapport, Samuel, and Wright, H. (eds.), *A Treasury of Science*. New York: Harper, 1958.

Andrade, E. N. da C., "The Birth of the Nuclear Atom," *Scientific American,* November, 1956.

Darrow, Karl K., "The Quantum Theory," *Scientific American,* March, 1952.

Feinberg, G., and Goldhaber, M., "Conservation Laws," *Scientific American,* October, 1963.

Gamow, George, "The Principle of Uncertainty," *Scientific American,* January, 1958.

———, "The Exclusion Principle," *Scientific American,* July, 1959.

Gell-Mann, Murray, and Rosenbaum, E. P., "Elementary Particles," *Scientific American,* July, 1957.

Hahn, Otto, "The Discovery of Fission," *Scientific American,* February, 1958.

Hill, R. D., "Resonance Particles," *Scientific American,* January, 1963.

Marshak, Robert E., "The Multiplicity of Particles," *Scientific American,* January, 1952.

———, "Pions," *Scientific American,* January, 1957.

Morrison, Philip, "The Neutrino," *Scientific American,* January, 1956.

Seaborg, Glenn T., and Perlman, I., "The Synthetic Elements," *Scientific American,* April, 1950.

Seaborg, Glenn T., and Ghiorso, Albert., "The Newest Elements," *Scientific American,* December, 1956.

Seaborg, Glenn T., and Fritsch, A. R., "The Synthetic Elements: III," *Scientific American,* April, 1963.

Segrè, Emilio, and Wiegand, Clyde E., "The Antiproton," *Scientific American,* June, 1956.

Wilson, Robert R., "Particle Accelerators," *Scientific American,* March, 1958.

Yagoda, Herman, "The Tracks of Nuclear Particles," *Scientific American,* May, 1956.

INDEX

191

Crookes, Sir William, 44, 63, 92
Curie, Eve, 53, 56, 127
Curie, Irène, 52, 56-57, 127-131, 134, 136, 138, 141, 158, 161
Curie, Marie, 50-57, 65, 68, 76, 102, 127-128
Curie, Pierre, 51-57, 70, 102, 127
Curium (element 96), 167-168, 171, 173-175
Cyclotron, 123-126, 165-167

Dalton, John, 24-29, 38-39, 49, 62
Davisson, C. J., 111
De Broglie, Louis, 110-111, 114
Definite proportions, Law of, 24-25
Democritus of Abdera, 13-19, 23-24, 41
Dempster, A. J., 94
Deuteron, 151-153
Dirac, P. A. M., 111, 115, 129, 177

Einstein, Albert, 100, 102-103, 109-110, 114, 117-119, 126, 130, 134, 140, 145-146, 168
Einsteinium (element 99), 168-169, 173, 175
Electricity, Static, 41-42
Electromagnetic radiation, 60-62, 69, 72, 96, 99-104, 110-111, 114
Electron, 61-62, 64-66, 71-72, 78-79, 82-84, 88-89, 91, 98-115, 121, 129-130, 176-177, 180, 184, 188
Element, Chemical, 20-21, 27-28
Empedocles, 11-12, 17, 23
Energy, 100-101, 117-119, 130, 178; see also Atomic energy
Exclusion principle, 114-115

Faraday, Michael, 59-61, 159
Fermi, Enrico, 132-137, 140-141, 144-150, 158, 168, 179
Fermium (element 100), 168-172, 175
Flerov, Georgi, 172-173
Four elements, Theory of, 11-12, 17-18
Francium (element 87), 164
Frequency, Electromagnetic, 69, 99-101, 110
Fresnel, Augustin Jean, 59
Frisch, Otto, 138-140, 150, 158

Gamma ray, 72, 74-75, 96, 101, 110, 130, 177, 188
Geiger, Hans, 73, 80, 96
Geiger counter, 74, 149, 160
Geissler, Heinrich, 43
Germer, L. H., 111
Glendenin, L. E., 163

Hahn, Otto, 137-140, 145, 150, 158
Half-life, 75-76, 162-163
Harkins, William D., 95, 97
Heisenberg, Werner, 111-115, 132, 145, 181-182
Hertz, Heinrich, 61, 99
Hertzian waves, see Radio waves
Hiroshima, 7, 155
Huygens, Christian, 58-59

Ion, 70
Isotope, 94-95, 97, 128

Jeans, James, 74-75, 82
Joliot, Frédéric, 127-132, 134, 136, 138, 141, 146, 158, 161

Kirchoff, Gustaf, 59

Langmuir, Irving, 105-108, 115
Lavoisier, Antoine, 22-23
Lawrence, Ernest Orlando, 123-125, 132, 172
Lawrencium (element 103), 172, 175
Lenard, Philipp, 44-45, 47, 78-79, 81
Leucippus, 12-14, 19
Lewis, Gilbert N., 105, 152
Light, 58-63, 69, 99, 102-103, 110
Lorentz, H. A., 62, 66, 99
Lucretius, 16, 18-19

MacKenzie, K. R., 162
Marconi, Guglielmo, 61
Marinsky, J. A., 163
Marsden, Ernest, 80
Marshak, Robert E., 182
Mass number, 94-95, 97-98, 142, 177
Mass spectrograph, 93-94
Maxwell, James Clerk, 59-61, 99
McMillan, Edwin M., 150-152, 161, 165
Meitner, Lise, 137-140, 150, 158
Mendeleev, Dmitri Ivanovich, 31-39, 108, 170
Mendelevium (element 101), 170, 175
Meson, 182-184, 187-188
Meyer, Lothar, 31, 35
Millikan, Robert A., 109, 129
Molecule, 27-28
Moseley, H. G. J., 86-87
Multiple proportions, Law of, 25

Nagasaki, 7, 155
Neptunium (element 93), 151, 153, 161, 164-166, 175
Neutrino, 179-181, 183-184, 187-188
Neutron, 95-98, 120, 122, 127-128, 131-

The Author

ROBERT SILVERBERG has been a full-time free-lance writer since he graduated from Columbia University in 1956. He has been writing professionally since 1953, currently doing nonfiction paperback originals as well as books for young people. His two latest books for Putnam are *The Great Doctors*, and *Socrates*.

Mr. Silverberg's hobbies include travel and collecting classical music records. He has visited Europe several times, traveled widely in the United States and Caribbean area, and in the near future hopes to travel to Asia and Africa. He, his wife and their three cats live in a huge, book-filled old house once owned by Fiorello LaGuardia, in Riverdale, New York.